15 to 1

2000 for 2000

BOOKS

First published in 2000 by Channel 4 Books, an imprint of Macmillan Publishers Ltd, 25 Eccleston Place, London SW1W 9NF, Basingstoke and Oxford.

Associated companies throughout the world.

www.macmillan.co.uk

ISBN 0 7522 7230 6

Text © Channel 4 Books, 2000

9 8 7 6

A CIP catalogue record for this book is available from the British Library.

Design and typesetting by Ben Cracknell Studios.
Printed in the EC.

This book accompanies the television series *15 to 1* made by Regent Productions for Channel 4.
Executive producer: William G. Stewart

15–1 is a Trademark of Regent Productions Limited. Licensed by Pearson Television Enterprises.

CONTENTS

HOW TO
Play

15 to 1

15 to 1: 2000 for 2000 is the ultimate challenge for you either to test your own general knowledge, or to pit your wits against friends and family. The book contains 2000 questions, all of which have featured on the television show. They are divided into three rounds, to enable you to recreate the show at home.

If you are playing in a group of three or more you need to nominate one of the players to take the role of William G. Stewart and act as questionmaster and scorekeeper. There are scoresheets at the back of the book (pages 251–272) which you can either photocopy or fill in with pencil.

For eight players upward

Although we always start with fifteen players on the programme, it is quite possible to play the same game with only eight (providing not too many players lose both their lives in Round One!).

Round One

Each player starts the game with three lives. In turn, the questionmaster asks each player a question from the Round One section (pages 11–50). If the player answers incorrectly, or does not know the answer, they lose a life. A second question is then asked of each player in turn, and again, lives are lost for incorrect answers. At the end of the round, any players who have lost two lives are out of the game.

Round Two

The remaining players begin the next round with either two or three lives, depending on whether they got both questions right in Round One. The questionmaster begins by asking the first person a question from Round Two (pages 51–134). If the player gets the answer wrong, or cannot answer, they lose a life and play moves on to the next player. If the player gives the correct answer, they can then nominate another player to answer a question. If this player gets the question right, then he or she can nominate another player and so play continues. However, if any player gets a question wrong, then he or she loses a life and play returns to the previous player to nominate another player again. Play continues until all but three of the players have lost all of their lives.

Round Three

The remaining three players proceed to the quick-fire Round Three, with three new lives. In this round, not only do the players have to avoid losing lives, they also need to gain points. The questionmaster will need a pencil and paper to keep score. For every incorrect answer the player loses a life; for every correct answer he or she gains 10 points.

The questionmaster begins play by asking questions from Round Three (pages 135–192) to the floor – the quickest correct answer gains 10 points. An incorrect answer results in a life lost. This continues until one of the players has earned 30 points.

From then on, a correct answer allows the player to either answer another question, or to nominate another player. If the player gets the question wrong, then the next question is to the floor again. If a player chooses to nominate and the second player gets the question right, then the second player has the option to take a question or nominate, and so on. If a nominated player gets the question wrong, then play returns to the previous player who can choose either to take a question or to nominate again. If the player who answered the question from the floor chooses to take a question rather than nominate, and gets this wrong, play returns to the floor.

Play continues until two of the players have lost all three lives. The questionmaster continues to ask the final player questions until either they have lost all three lives, or a total of 40 questions have been asked during Round Three. The winner is the player who has the highest score.

For five to eight players

If you have between five and eight players, including the questionmaster, then you can play a two-round game, following the instructions above for Round Two and Round Three. Each player begins Round Two (now the first round) with three lives.

For three to four players

For just three or four players, including the questionmaster, play Round Three only. If you want the game to be slightly easier, use the questions from Round One.

For two players

If there are just two players, each player should take a turn at being the questionmaster. At the beginning of the game, the players should agree which round they are going to take the questions from. The questionmaster asks the other player questions, awarding 10 points for a correct answer, and deducting a life for an incorrect answer. When the first player has lost all their lives or a total of 40 questions have been asked, they take a turn as the questionmaster and ask the second player questions, until all three of this player's lives are lost or 40 questions have been asked. The winner is the player with the most points.

15 to 1

ROUND ONE
Questions

1 *Children's Stories*

What is the name of the Bogeyman in the picture book by Raymond Briggs?

2 *The USA*

Which part of the USA lies within the Arctic Circle?

3 *Medicine*

Chronic Fatigue Syndrome is more commonly known by what two-letter term?

4 *Geography*

In terms of population (13 million), which is the largest capital city on the continent of Africa?

5 *Popular Songs*

'Jerusalem' is a musical setting by Hubert Parry of a poem by which English writer?

6 *English Cities*

Nelson's flagship, HMS *Victory*, the Tudor warship, *Mary Rose*, and Britain's first 'ironclad warship', HMS *Warrior*: which city are they all in?

7 *Television*

What are the first names of Richard Dimbleby's two sons, who followed him into current affairs broadcasting?

8 *Musical Instruments*

To help the player, on which orchestral instrument are the 'C' strings coloured red and the 'F' strings coloured black?

9 *The Arts*

What did John Christie build in the grounds of his estate near Lewes in East Sussex, and open to audiences in 1934?

10 *Sport*

Odsal Stadium in Bradford, The Willows in Salford, Central Park in Wigan: which sport is played at these venues?

11 *Films of the 1990s*

The 1986 film *Manhunter*, based on a novel by Thomas Harris, was the first to feature the character Hannibal Lecter. Which multiple-Oscar-winning film of 1991 was the second?

12 *Television*

John Lithgow, Jane Curtin and Kristen Johnston star in which American comedy series that follows an alien mission on Earth?

13 *Mathematics*

What name is given to the branch of mathematics that deals with the properties of lines, points, surfaces and solids?

14 *Biology*

In biological classification, 'species' is the smallest group. What is the largest?

15 *Twentieth-century Theatre*

What is the name of the Liverpool-born playwright whose plays include *Amadeus*, *Lettice and Lovage* and *The Gift of the Gorgon*?

16 *The Natural World*

On which island country in the Indian Ocean did the dodo live until it became extinct in the late seventeenth century?

17 *Parliament*

By what name is the official report of debates in Lords and Commons better known?

18 *Astronomy*

What is the name of the galaxy in which our solar system lies?

19 *Words*

What Latin phrase literally means 'for the rate'?

20 *Computer Technology*

What does CD-ROM stand for?

21 *Films of the 1990s*

Waterworld in 1995, *The Postman* in 1997 and *Message in a Bottle* in 1999: which Hollywood actor links these films?

22 *The Bible*

In the gospel of St John, what miracle did Jesus perform at Siloam, a pool in Jerusalem?

23 *Botany*

Lonicera is the Latin name for which popular fragrant climbing shrub?

24 Famous Quotes

'Television has brought back murder into the home – where it belongs.' The words of which famous British film director who specialized in thrillers?

25 Twentieth-century Literature

In which novel by Anthony Burgess is the storyteller a 15-year-old hooligan called Alex, using a teenage slang 'Nadsat'?

26 Theatre

What is the name of the eponymous character in a George Bernard Shaw play who is an officer in the Salvation Army?

27 The British Monarchy

Which Scottish bodyguard (a Royal Company) is in attendance on the sovereign when she is at Holyrood House?

28 The UK

Apart from London, only three cities in the UK have underground railway systems. Name two of the three.

29 The USA

Which is the only one of New York City's five boroughs to be located on the mainland?

30 European Monarchy

A monarchy until April 1931 – a monarchy again from November 1975. Which European country?

31 Awards

What is the two-word inscription below the Royal Crown on the Victoria Cross?

32 Musicals

While on a hunting holiday, two Americans, Tommy Allbright and Jeff Douglas, stray into a Scottish highland village that only comes to life for one day every hundred years: in which Lerner and Loewe musical?

33 The Bible

Which famous story is told in Genesis chapters 6, 7, 8 and 9?

34 Tennis

The French Open is played at which venue in Paris?

35 *Patriotic Songs*

Which song begins with the lines 'When Britain first, at Heaven's command/Arose from out the azure main'?

36 *Number Systems*

What is the highest digit that can appear in the octal number system?

37 *Literature*

In which series of adventure stories are John Clayton and Jane Porter leading characters?

38 *Inventions*

For the invention of what is the British inventor Trevor Baylis best known?

39 *Furniture*

What French word is given to a full-length mirror mounted on swivels within a frame?

40 *Latin Terms*

What Latin word meaning 'let it be done' is used for a decree, a formal command or a short order or warrant of a judge?

41 *Gemstones*

What name is given to the green gem variety of the mineral beryl?

42 *Medicine*

Exsanguination is a severe loss of what?

43 *The UK*

Dartmoor lies wholly in which English county?

44 *History of the USA*

What is the name of the fort in San Antonio, where in 1836 a famous battle took place between Mexican troops and volunteers fighting for Texan independence?

45 *World War Two*

What name was given to the joint declaration of August 1941, made by Winston Churchill and Franklin Roosevelt, following a series of conferences at sea?

46 *Medicine*

A cytometer is an instrument for counting and measuring what in the human body?

47 *Decades*

In which decade of the twentieth century did Concorde make its maiden flight, was colour television introduced in the UK and the Open University founded?

48 *Computers*

In computer terminology, what does FAQ stand for?

49 *Twentieth-century Literature*

Midnight's Children, *The Moor's Last Sigh* and *The Satanic Verses* are works by which author?

50 *Awards*

What is the name of the statuette awarded at an annual ceremony by the American Academy of Television Arts and Sciences?

51 *Twentieth-century Theatre*

Which play by Edward Albee examines the marriage of George, a history lecturer, and Martha, the wealthy college president's daughter?

52 *Geography*

Hamilton is the capital of which British Dependent Territory?

53 *Classical Music*

Which ballet (with music by Delibes) has the alternative title *The Girl with Enamel Eyes*?

54 *Greek Mythology*

Who was the goddess of witch-craft and black magic in Greek mythology, who presided at crossroads, and who the ancient Greeks associated with evil?

55 *Australia*

Which territory of Australia is known, for short, as the ACT?

56 *Religion*

What is the indigenous religion of Japan?

57 *History of Medicine*

Two London hospitals – both with the prefix 'Royal' – were founded in the nineteenth century by William Marsden. One is the Royal Marsden, what is the other?

58 *Music*

In the Gilbert and Sullivan opera *Princess Ida*, of what sort of institution is Princess Ida the head?

59 *The Calendar*

Which season, in the northern hemisphere, runs from the vernal equinox to the summer solstice?

60 *The UK*

Extending 256 miles from Edale in Derbyshire to Kirk Yetholm on the Scottish border, which was the UK's first designated long-distance path?

61 *The USA*

Augusta is the capital of which state?

62 *Science*

Which pigment produces the green colour in plants?

63 *Show Business*

What is the name of the singer-showman known to millions as Mr Moonlight, who died in September 1999, aged 71?

64 *Horse Racing*

How many of the five English Classics are run at Epsom?

65 *Music*

What name is given to the ability possessed by some people to identify and reproduce a note without reference to a tuned musical pitch?

66 *The UK*

The picturesque Gower Peninsula is within the boundary of which city?

67 *Science*

What name is given to the process of holding milk at around 72°C for 15 seconds and then rapidly cooling it, to destroy disease-causing bacteria?

68 *The Twelfth Century*

Which twelfth-century king of England was seized by Leopold V on his way back from the Holy Land, and only released after a ransom of 150,000 marks, raised by his English subjects, was paid?

69 *The USA*

What is the collective name of the group of islands that includes Key Largo, Long Key, Big Pine Key, Sugarloaf Key and Key West?

70 *Astronomy*

Charon is the only moon of which planet in our solar system?

71 *Law*

What name is given to those periods of the year when it is prohibited to kill or take game, freshwater fish, sea fish or oysters?

72 *Horse Racing*

The King Edward VII Stakes, the St James's Palace Stakes and the Coronation Stakes are all run at which annual meeting held in June?

73 *The Bible*

Literally meaning 'Gate of God', what name is given in the book of Genesis chapter 10 to the city founded by Nimrod, in ancient Babylonia?

74 *Music*

In which Yorkshire city is the National Centre for Popular Music?

75 *The Royal Family*

What is the brand name under which Prince Charles markets his organic produce?

76 *Literature*

Who wrote the novel *Dr Zhivago*?

77 *The Holy Roman Empire*

The Knight's War, the Peasant's War, the Ghent Revolt and the abdication of Charles V all occurred during which century?

78 *Poetry*

What is the name of the poet who died in Ravenna in Italy in 1321, whose best-known work is probably *The Divine Comedy*?

79 *Myth and Legend*

In Scottish folklore, what is the name of the water spirit, usually in the form of a horse, that appears as a warning to those destined to be drowned?

80 *The Seventeenth Century*

Why is 30 January 1649 a famous date in English history?

81 *Europe*

The three member states to have joined the European Union most recently did so in 1995. Name two of the three.

82 *Computing*

In computer terminology what does the acronym DOS stand for?

83 *Medicine*

Oto-rhino laryngology is known by three much more manageable initials. What are they?

84 *British and American History*

What title is shared by the 1689 British statute enshrining the constitutional principles won during the Glorious Revolution and the first ten amendments to the American Constitution?

85 *The Royal Family*

Who is the mother of Lady Sarah Chatto?

86 *Sport*

In the parade at the opening ceremony of the summer Olympic Games, which country always enters the stadium first?

87 *Latin Phrases*

Which Latin phrase meaning 'winner of the games' is often applied to a school's sports champion?

88 *Sport*

The Castleford Tigers, the Hull Sharks and the Wigan Warriors are major clubs in which sport?

89 *Chemistry*

Co is the symbol for which chemical element?

90 *The UK*

Which island in the Bristol Channel is designated as a statutory Marine Nature Reserve?

91 *Sport*

The Briton Jonathan Edwards holds a world record of 18.29 metres in which event?

92 *Mythology*

What is the name of the king who turned everything he touched to gold?

93 *The Bible*

Two books of the Bible are named after women. Name one of the two.

94 *Geography*

Some 44,000 square miles in area, which is the largest island in the Caribbean?

95 *Television*

In which fictional Manchester suburb is Coronation Street set?

96 *Japanese History*

What term was used to denote the warrior class, which dominated Japanese government between the twelfth and nineteenth centuries?

97 *Music*

With which musical instrument are the names Paul Tortelier, Mstislav Rostropovich and Jacqueline du Pré associated?

98 *The Christian Calendar*

What name is given to the day in the Christian calendar that falls before Good Friday?

99 *Television/Theatre*

How is Paul O'Grady better known to theatre and television audiences?

100 *Geography*

The New Forest is part of which English county?

101 *Abbreviations*

In the world of finance, what do the initials RPI stand for?

102 *Geography*

What is the capital of Kenya?

103 *Pop Music*

The albums *The Colour of My Love*, *Unison* and *Let's Talk About Love* are bestsellers for which female star?

104 *Politics*

What is the minimum age at which someone may stand for parliament?

105 *Medicine*

A person with the initials FRCP after his or her name is a member of the Royal College of… what?

106 *Museums*

A museum celebrating the lives and works of which family is at Haworth Parsonage in Yorkshire?

107 *Shakespeare*

In which play do the characters Benvolio, Mercutio and Tybalt appear?

108 *Medicine*

Osteoporosis is the thinning and weakening of which components of the human body?

109 *Poetry*

Ted Hughes' last major collection, *Birthday Letters*, is a reflection on his relationship with his first wife. What was her name?

110 *Sport*

In the Olympics, what is the shortest distance, in metres, over which swimming races are held?

111 *Science*

In computing, eight bits usually make one what?

112 *Geography*

What is the popular name of the famous eighteenth-century opera house in Milan?

113 *Foreign Phrases*

What, in common use, is the French phrase meaning 'that's life'?

114 *Classical Music*

Who composed *Cosi Fan Tutte* and *Don Giovanni*?

115 *History*

What family relation was Richard I to King John?

116 *Television*

Die-hard fans of which popular comedy series on BBC2 are known as Dwarfers?

117 *History*

In ancient Greece and Rome, for what was a hippodrome chiefly used?

118 Roman Mythology

Who is the Roman goddess of love, identified with the Greek goddess Aphrodite?

119 Geography

Into which ocean do the rivers Euphrates, Tigris and Irrawaddy flow?

120 The Media

What are Discovery, Granada Breeze and National Geographic?

121 Saints' Days

When is St David's Day?

122 The USA

In which city in Tennessee is the 'Grand Ole Opry'?

123 Popular Literature

Who is the author of the novels Jamaica Inn, My Cousin Rachel and Rebecca?

124 Education

There are three universities in Glasgow including the University of Glasgow founded in 1451. Name one of the other two.

125 English Law

A coroner has to be a member of five years' standing in either of which two professions?

126 Words

Graphology is a study that interprets personality and character from what?

127 The USA

The six states of Rhode Island, Connecticut, Massachusetts, New Hampshire, Maine and Vermont make up a region known as what?

128 The Seventeenth Century

Who, 350 years ago, declared England a Commonwealth and abolished the monarchy?

129 The UK

Its ancient capital was Castletown, its present capital is Douglas: which Crown dependency?

130 Food and Drink

What in Spain are 'tapas'?

131 *Geography*

If you fly directly from Paris in France to Milan in Italy, which third country do you fly over?

132 *The Media*

The name of which French newspaper translates as 'the world'?

133 *Famous Advertising Slogans*

'The United Colours of…' what?

134 *Sport*

Which country's national rugby union team are known as the Springboks?

135 *Education*

In which city is the University of the West of England?

136 *The Royal Family*

What is the first Christian name, and surname, of Princess Anne's son?

137 *Mythology*

What was the name of the Greek god of the sea?

138 *European Monarchy*

The House of Orange-Nassau is the ruling house in which European country?

139 *Geography*

Which of the 10 greatest or longest rivers of the world flows into the Mediterranean?

140 *Music*

Whose four operas *The Rhinegold*, *The Valkyrie*, *Siegfried* and *The Twilight of the Gods* are collectively known as *The Ring* or *Ring Cycle*?

141 *Chemistry*

What does it mean if a substance is described as being anhydrous?

142 *Sport*

In which sport are Eddie Irvine, Johnny Herbert and David Coulthard all well-known names in the UK?

143 *Computers*

AOL is the largest Internet service provider in the world. What does AOL stand for?

144 *Religion*

What name was given to the sacred writings of a breakaway Jewish sect, found in 1947 on the shores of the Dead Sea, which included much of the Hebrew Bible and rules for the life of the sect?

145 *Literature*

In which story by Roald Dahl does a deprived orphan boy find friendship and happiness when a magic giant fruit grows in his garden?

146 *Charles Dickens*

How is the character Jack Dawkins better known in a Dickens novel?

147 *Science*

What name is given to the branch of zoology that deals with birds and their behaviour?

148 *Exploration*

In which Commonwealth country are there mountain ranges named after the English explorer Matthew Flinders?

149 *The Sixteenth Century*

Who was on the English throne when Shakespeare and Oliver Cromwell were born?

150 *Bond Films*

What is the name of the actress who was covered in gold paint in *Goldfinger*?

151 *Music*

Who was the composer of the *St Matthew Passion*, first performed in Leipzig in 1729?

152 *History*

Where in the UK will you find the stone that, according to Celtic legend, was used as a pillow by Jacob when he beheld the visions of angels?

153 *World War One*

What event at sea, on 7 May 1915, led to the deaths of 1198 people, including 128 Americans?

154 *Classic Science Fiction*

How is the brilliant scientist Griffen described in the title of an H.G. Wells' novel of 1897?

155 *History of South America*

Which is the only country in South America that was originally established as a Portuguese colony?

156 *Ancient History*

Roxana was the wife of which ancient Macedonian king?

157 *Colonial Africa*

Chad, Niger and Mali all achieved full independence in 1960 from which European colonial power?

158 *Decades*

The League of Nations was founded, the British Broadcasting Corporation was established and the Winter Olympics were first staged in which decade?

159 *Athletics*

Which Dutch athlete, who won four Olympic gold medals at the 1958 Games in London, did the IAF name as their female Athlete of the Century?

160 *Religion*

Which Mediterranean island, on which Paul was shipwrecked, is called, in the Bible, Melita?

161 *Mythology*

In Greek mythology, Selene was the goddess of what?

162 *The British Monarchy*

Four kings have sat on the throne this century. Who is the only one not to have been Prince of Wales?

163 *Literature*

How many tales are there in Chaucer's *Canterbury Tales*?

164 *Awards and Decorations*

On the list of which Order, restricted to 65 ordinary members, will you find the names of Sir David Attenborough, Sir Alec Guinness and David Hockney?

165 *Greek Mythology*

What is the name of the lion, the killing of which was one of the 12 labours of Hercules?

166 *The Bible*

Who, on a visit to King Solomon, gave him a gift of 120 talents of gold, spices and precious stones?

167 *Demographics*

The population of which continent, which has tripled to 767 million since 1960, is the world's fastest growing?

168 *Environment*

What do the initials SSSI stand for?

169 *Sport and the Royal Family*

Which member of the royal family, a first cousin of the Queen, is President of the All England Lawn Tennis and Croquet Club?

170 *Geography*

Which, at 240 miles, is the longest river in the geographical British Isles?

171 *Commonwealth*

Formerly called Salisbury, which city is the capital of Zimbabwe?

172 *Civil Aviation*

Aeroflot is the national carrier in which country?

173 *English Law*

What term is used in English law to refer to the questioning of witnesses called by the other side in a case?

174 *Motorways*

The M27 links which two cities on the south coast?

175 *Cities*

Which Middle Eastern city is bounded by the Golden Gate, Herod's Gate, Jaffa Gate and Zion Gate?

176 *Children's Literature*

Who created the fictional Scatterbrook Farm on which stands Worzel Gummidge?

177 *Sea Areas*

Which of the sea areas, used in the BBC shipping forecasts, lies furthest away from the British Isles in the Atlantic Ocean past Portugal?

178 *British Politics*

Harold Wilson resigned as Prime Minister in 1976; who took over as Prime Minister?

179 *Government*

Although commonly known as the Foreign Office, that is not its full name. What is the correct name?

180 *Motorways*

A journey round the M25, onto the M23 going south, will take you to which major airport in West Sussex?

181 *Science*

Which acid is a constituent of vinegar?

182 *Geography*

In which Commonwealth country are the Southern Alps and the Canterbury Plains?

183 *Meteorology*

What name is given to the hot period between early July and mid-August when Sirius rises and sets with the sun?

184 *Theatre*

In the theatre what does the abbreviation FOH stand for?

185 *English Cathedrals*

At 404 feet high, which is England's tallest cathedral spire?

186 *History*

Only four crowned English monarchs since the Norman conquest have been given no regnal number. Name two of the four.

187 *The Royal Family*

Her Christian names are Anne Elizabeth Alice Louise. What's her surname?

188 *Music*

What is the name of the stringed instrument named after the Greek god of the winds?

189 *Famous Seconds*

Ramsay MacDonald, in 1924, became the first man to lead a Labour government in the UK. Who, in 1945, became the second man to do so?

190 *Politics*

In American and Australian politics, what does the abbreviation MHR stand for?

191 *Pen Names*

What was the real name of the American writer Mark Twain?

192 *English Law*

Which legal term is used for the right to unobstructed light or windows protected by this right?

193 *Art*

Containing more than 12,000 sculptures, 16,000 paintings and 600,000 drawings and works on paper, which is the largest public collection of art in the world?

194 *Politics*

Govan, Rutherglen and Springburn are parliamentary constituencies in which city?

195 *Geography*

Botafogo, Flamengo, Ipanema and Copacabana are all areas of which South American city?

196 *Castles*

Walmer Castle, Hever Castle and Leeds Castle are in which English county?

197 *English and Irish History*

Which sixteenth-century English king first took the title King of Ireland?

198 *Twentieth-century Literature*

His novels include *Metroland* (1980), *Staring at the Sun* (1986) and *A History of the World in 10 ½ Chapters*. Who is this English writer?

199 *Science and Technology*

Thermal, Fast Breeder and Advanced Gas-Cooled are all types of what?

200 *Mythology*

Who, in Arthurian mythology, is Uther Pendragon?

201 *Language*

What is the meaning of the Latin phrase *ceteris paribus*?

202 *Plants*

The essential oil Neroli, used in perfumery, is obtained from the flowers of which fruit?

203 *Music*

Which opera by Sergey Prokofiev is based on a novel by Leo Tolstoy?

204 *The Legal System*

The holder of which office is the most senior judge in the Court of Appeal?

205 *Shakespeare*

Which eponymous hero of a Shakespeare play describes himself as 'one that lov'd not wisely but too well'?

206 *Words*

What, in a theatre, is a 'loge'?

207 *Sport*

Which British city will stage the Commonwealth Games of 2002?

208 *English Law*

Piscary is a right concerning what activity?

209 *Sport in the UK*

In which sport is the Sekonda Superleague the premier league?

210 *Geography*

The largest of which island group, off the southern tip of South America, is divided between Argentina and Chile?

211 *Twentieth-century Britain*

Britain was served by two prime ministers during World War One. Name them both.

212 *Medicine*

Roentgenotherapy is a form of healing using what?

213 *Protest Groups*

What is the name of the Welsh protest group, active since 1979, which is against what they perceive to be England's treatment of Wales as a colonial possession?

214 *History of Medicine*

What is the name of the first test-tube baby, born in Oldham in 1978?

215 *Geography*

Which Alpine pass between Switzerland and Italy is based on a road built by Napoleon early in the nineteenth century?

216 *Operetta*

In which Gilbert and Sullivan operetta does a witch's curse oblige the holder of the baronetcy to commit a crime every day?

217 *Geography*

The longest suspension bridge in The UK is over 1,400 metres in length. Which river in the east of England does it cross?

218 *The Brontës*

What is the name of the resident at Wuthering Heights, found as a waif in the streets of Liverpool, and brought up at the house by the Earnshaw family?

219 *Musicals*

'That'll be the Day', 'Peggy Sue' and 'Oh Boy' are hit numbers from which long-running musical in London's West End?

220 *Zoology*

In zoological terms, what does 'lanate' mean?

221 *Cinema*

Jane Horrocks starred in the title role of which 1998 film in which she impersonates the singing of Judy Garland, Shirley Bassey and Marlene Dietrich?

222 *The 1950s*

Which Asian conflict ended with an Armistice signed at Panmunjon on 27 July 1953?

223 *Music*

From which country does a piece of music or a dance known as the gavotte originate?

224 *Television Actresses*

Who was the actress, a former *Brookside* teenager, who landed a role in the play *Closer* and took Broadway by storm?

225 *The Bible*

Which Old Testament book is divided into 150 parts, of which 73 are attributed to David?

226 Meteorology

What name is given in meteorology to the boundary between two air masses of different temperature and humidity?

227 The UK

Bolingbroke Castle, Market Rasen racecourse and the seaside resort of Skegness are all in which county?

228 Festivals

Which Hindu festival has a name which translates as 'garland of lights'?

229 Human Anatomy

How is the clavicle more commonly known?

230 Science

What name is given to the science and technology of space flight?

231 Jewellery

What generic name is given to the yellowish fossilized resin from trees used for jewellery?

232 The Olympics

In which Olympic sport are there categories called Finn, International Tornado and International Star?

233 The English Monarchy

Which king of England united the rival houses of York and Lancaster by marrying Elizabeth, daughter of Edward IV?

234 Theatre

Caroline drama is drama from which century?

235 Aviation

Which two cities in the north of England are served by the airport with the code LBA?

236 The English Monarchy

What was the name of the Archbishop of Canterbury who crowned Elizabeth II in 1953?

237 Geography

The Cyclades and the Sporades: to which country do these groups of islands in the Mediterranean belong?

238 *Professional Boxing*

Under the British Boxing Board of Control's rules, which weight division lies above Light Heavyweight and below Heavyweight?

239 *Scientific Conundrums*

The British mathematician, Andrew Wiles, achieved fame in the 1990s with his solution to which celebrated mathematical problem, known by the abbreviation FLT?

240 *Epic Literature*

The epic Indian poem, the *Mahabharata*, was written in which ancient Indian language?

241 *The Bible*

The death of Moses is recorded in the fifth book of Moses. Which book is that?

242 *Music*

Thespis, or *The Gods Grown Old*, in 1871, was the first. *The Grand Duke*, in 1896, was the last collaboration of which team of lyricist and composer?

243 *Film Actors*

He has been a Detroit cop in Los Angeles, a nutty chemistry professor with a weight problem and a doctor with an uncanny ability to talk to animals: which American comedy actor?

244 *Geography*

What is the name of the bay or inlet of the North Sea that lies between Norfolk and Lincolnshire?

245 *The UK*

Blyth, Morpeth and Berwick-upon-Tweed are three of the largest towns in which English county?

246 *The New Testament*

How are the gospels of Matthew, Mark and Luke referred to because of the many similarities between them?

247 *Greek Mythology*

Who in mythology killed his father, married his mother and had four daughters, one of whom was called Antigone?

248 *Africa*

The Kikuyu are the dominant ethnic group in which East African country?

249 *Classical Music*

What kind of musical composition are Mozart's *Prague*, Haydn's *Philosopher* and Mahler's *Resurrection*?

250 *History of the FA Cup*

Bert Turner of Charlton Athletic in 1946, Tommy Hutchison of Manchester City in 1981 and Gary Mabbut of Spurs in 1987: what odd distinction did they all manage in the FA Cup final of those years?

251 *The Media*

Which national weekly magazine, founded in 1868, consists entirely of advertisements for buying and selling?

252 *The Bible*

'O my son Absalom, would God I had died for thee!' Which king of Israel weeps thus for his dead son?

253 *Modern Warfare*

With what type of warfare is the Wiltshire research establishment Porton Down chiefly associated?

254 *The Royal Family*

Princess Alice and Prince Andrew were the parents of which member of the royal family?

255 *Latin Words and Phrases*

Often seen in books of quotations, what does the abbreviation ibid. or ib. mean?

256 *European Cities*

Authorities in Venice have approved an ambitious project to raise which famous part of the city by 14 inches and to seal it with a membrane to protect it from increasing flooding?

257 *Fiction*

Which famous fictional diarist is, in his latest volume, aged $30\frac{1}{4}$ and the head chef in a Soho restaurant called Hoi Polloi, specializing in offal and rude service?

258 *The British Monarchy*

Who was the last monarch to succeed his mother to the throne?

259 *Christian Sects*

What is unusual about the observance of the Sabbath by the Seventh Day Adventists?

260 *The USA*

What, in the USA, are Eastern Standard, Central Standard, Pacific Standard and Mountain?

261 *Finance*

Which London institution has the motto *Dictum meum pactum* which translates as 'My word is my bond'?

262 *The UK*

The Royal Military Academy is the British Army officer training college. By what name is it commonly known?

263 *Shakespeare*

In *A Midsummer Night's Dream*, Titania is the Queen of the Fairies, Hippolyta is Queen of… what or whom?

264 *International Finance*

What's the name of the Tokyo Stock Exchange index?

265 *The UK*

The Outer Bank, the Sarsen Circle and the Bluestone Circle are features of which famous heritage site?

266 *Medicine*

Which British university is named after the designer of the Great Western Railway?

267 *Literature*

Who was the author of the 'Waverley' novels, published in the nineteenth century?

268 *The UK*

At which main rail terminus in London do Eurostar trains from Paris and Brussels arrive?

269 *Parks and Gardens*

In which park in London is there a work by George Frederick Watts entitled 'Physical Energy' and, most famously, Sir George Frampton's statue of Peter Pan?

270 *Corporate Mottoes*

'Nation shall speak peace unto nation.' Which organization has this motto?

271 *The UK*

Two English cathedrals are listed as World Heritage Sites: Canterbury and which other?

272 *Geography*

What name is given to the parallel of latitude that marks the northern boundary of the tropical zone?

273 *Ancient British History*

Which Queen of the Iceni poisoned herself after defeat by the Romans around 60 AD?

274 *Wildlife*

Pipistrelle, Whiskered and Horse-shoe are all common British species of which creature?

275 *Law*

What's the minimum age at which someone can adopt a child in England, Wales and Scotland?

276 *The Royal Family*

Which palace is the London home of the Prince of Wales?

277 *Newspapers*

In which city is the *Daily Record* published, the biggest-selling regional newspaper in the UK?

278 *Cocktails*

What would you add to a Virgin Mary to create a Bloody Mary?

279 *Russia*

Founded as St Petersburg, it became Petrograd, then Leningrad. What is this city now called?

280 *British Cities*

The Radcliffe Camera, the Carfax Tower and the Sheldonian Theatre are famous landmarks in which English city?

281 *The New Testament*

What was the name of the leper in whose house in Bethany Jesus rested on his final journey to Jerusalem?

282 Board Games

In which ancient game are there 136 standard playing pieces, or tiles, with most sets having eight bonus tiles representing the flowers or seasons?

283 The USA

Arlington, the national cemetery, the Pentagon and the headquarters of the CIA are in which state?

284 The Middle Ages

It is 230 feet long and almost 20 inches high. It portrays 626 people, 202 horses and 55 dogs. Which medieval work of art?

285 Art and Artists

Away from the Flock and *Mother and Child Divided* are two works by which controversial British sculptor and painter?

286 The Arts

Which post was held successively, in the first half of this century, by Alfred Austin, Robert Bridges and John Masefield and is now held by Andrew Motion?

287 Geography

The Isle of Wight, a county in its own right, lies due south of which county?

288 History of Pop

Which famous British pop group made their last public appearance in a roof-top performance in London in 1969?

289 Christianity

Which Latin term describes the route taken by Christ through Jerusalem to Calvary?

290 Political Parties

From 1973 to 1975 it was known as People and from 1975 it was The Ecology Party. In 1985 it changed its name to what?

291 London Tourist Attractions

Which popular London tourist attraction, which was first opened in 1835 by a French woman, is widely advertised by the slogan 'Who will you have a close encounter with?'

292 *Scottish Law*

The legal profession in Scotland is divided into two branches: solicitors and what?

293 *Greek Mythology*

Who, in Greek mythology, fled from Crete with his son Icarus, using wings made from feathers fastened with wax?

294 *English Law*

What term is used to refer to a person not concerned with a dispute, who is chosen by both sides to try to settle it?

295 *Business/Commerce*

Which British company is the country's largest provider of home mortgages and the largest holder of personal savings?

296 *History of England*

What event occurred in London between 2 and 5 September 1666?

297 *Geography*

What is the full and official title of the state of Australia?

298 Films of the 1990s

Andie MacDowell played Carrie, Simon Callow played Gareth, Kristen Scott-Thomas played Fiona and Hugh Grant played Charles. Which hit 1994 film was this?

299 *Historic Landmarks*

It runs from Bowness on the Solway Firth to Wallsend on the River Tyne, over a distance of approximately 75 miles. What is it?

300 *The Cinema*

The 1958 film *A Night to Remember* tells the story of a tragic incident in 1912 that was also the subject of which Oscar-winning 1997 film?

301 *The UK*

The towns of Wellingborough, Corby and Kettering are all in which county?

302 *Literary Quotations*

From Christopher Marlowe's *Dr Faustus*, whose face is it said 'launched a thousand ships'?

303 *Language*

Which European people speak a language called Euskara?

304 *James Bond Villains*

What is the name of Goldfinger's impassive bodyguard, whose favourite weapon was a bowler hat with a razor-sharp brim?

305 *Power and Energy*

What unit of power, still used when referring to the output of a car engine, is equivalent to 746 watts?

306 *Football*

Which English Premiership club play their home fixtures at Anfield?

307 *Business and Commerce*

The London-based firm Stanley Gibbons is known for dealing in what?

308 *Geography*

What is the name of the stretch of water that divides Tasmania from Australia?

309 *Shakespeare*

Instigated by the prophecy from three witches that he will become king, and urged on by his wife, which of Shakespeare's protagonists murders the King of Scotland and has himself proclaimed King?

310 *Name Connections*

What name connects Captain Kirk's logical Vulcan Science Officer aboard the Starship *Enterprise*, with the paediatrics guru who wrote *Baby and Child Care*?

311 *Greek Mythology*

From which creature did the cornucopia, or horn of plenty, come?

312 *Science*

Which Commonwealth country is the world's largest producer of uranium?

313 *The Legal Profession*

Which two letters after a barrister's name indicate that he or she has 'taken silk'?

314 *The UK*

What is the connection between Churchill Square in Brighton, Queensgate in Peterborough, Fosse Park in Leicester and Bluewater Park in Dartford?

315 *Science*

What was the nationality of the eighteenth-century astronomer Anders Celsius, after whom the temperature scale is named?

316 *The Bible*

In the Old Testament, who was the son of Abraham and Sarah, and the father of Jacob and Esau?

317 *Driving Licences*

At what age does a person's standard driving licence run out and from then have to be renewed every three years?

318 *Government*

Which government department is known by the abbreviation CMS?

319 *Politics*

Dhaka is the capital of which Asian Commonwealth country?

320 *Sport in the 1980s*

Alan Jones, Alan Prost and Nelson Piquet: with which sport would you associate these in the 1980s?

321 *History*

Which two royal houses in the fifteenth century both claimed possession of the English crown by right of descent from Edward III?

322 *Horse Racing*

In horse racing, how are the Cesarewitch and the Cambridgeshire known collectively?

323 *Official Duties*

Who, during their year in office, is officially the chief magistrate of the City of London?

324 *Education*

UCAS – or the Universities and Colleges Admissions Service – operates the central admissions scheme on behalf of all universities in the UK except one. Which one?

325 Legal Language

In the description of legal proceedings, R. versus Smith for example, what does the letter R stand for?

326 Airports

Schonefeld, Tegel and Tempelhof: which European capital city is served by these three airports?

327 Literature

The Strange Case of Dr Jekyll and Mr Hyde: who was the author?

328 Children's Television

Which creatures live under the ground of a London common but come out at night to pursue their environmentally friendly hobby of picking up rubbish left by humans?

329 Television

In which popular television programme do the studio audience vote by holding a picture of either a giant red tomato or a giant green pepper in the air?

330 History

In which two centuries did William Shakespeare live?

331 Literature

What's the name of the orphaned Indian child raised by animals in Rudyard Kipling's children's story The Jungle Book?

332 Space Exploration

The first was Salyut 1, launched by the Russians in 1971, then came Skylab, launched by the Americans in 1973, followed by Mir in 1986. What were Salyut 1, Skylab and Mir?

333 History

What nationality connects the composer Chopin, the scientist Marie Curie and the present Pope?

334 Sayings and Phrases

What common two-word term is given to the small zipped purse, attached to a belt, that was originally worn by skiers to hold their keys, but nowadays is a normal piece of street attire?

335 *Computer Technology*

Which manufacturer of computer hardware is known by its initials HP – for example on the HP laser jet printer?

336 *Politics*

With the politics of which Asian country are the names Jinnah, Zia and Bhutto associated?

337 *Geography*

Which island in the Pacific Ocean is famous for the more than 600 large stone statues on it?

338 *UK Cities*

Which is the UK's largest city, with an extensive canal system centred on Gas Street Basin, and a chocoholic's delight at Cadbury World, Bournville?

339 *Botany*

What term describes trees that shed their leaves when the growing season comes to an end?

340 *Laser Technology*

For what do the initials CVD stand?

341 *Europe*

Zeebrugge, Antwerp and Ostend are major ports in which European country?

342 *Films of the 1990s*

A 1990 film starring Mel Gibson and a 1996 film with Kenneth Branagh in the title role: two films based on which Shakespeare play?

343 *Children's Literature*

Who, in a series of books by Hugh Lofting, is the animal-loving hero who learned to talk to animals?

344 *Museums*

Which famous museum in Malibu, California, is named after the billionaire oil magnate who left it a huge legacy?

345 *Theatre*

Which long-running Agatha Christie play – it opened in 1952 and is still running – was once described by the *Guardian* as 'Cluedo dramatized for the theatre'?

346 *Medicine*

Pollinosis is a medical name for which common seasonal allergy?

347 *Ancient History*

The story of which queen of an ancient civilization has been told in drama by William Shakespeare, John Dryden and George Bernard Shaw?

348 *Medicine*

What are the teeth at the rear of the mouth used for grinding food called?

349 *Medical Equipment*

A gastroscope is an optical instrument used by physicians to inspect the interior of what?

350 *Population*

Which country has the largest population in the world – over 1 billion?

351 *English Law*

What colour badge, displayed on a disabled driver's windscreen, allows certain dispensations with regard to parking?

352 *Famous Landmarks*

Which famous seventeenth-century landmark is found in the Indian city of Agra?

353 *Currencies*

What is the name of the basic unit of currency used in Japan?

354 *Commonwealth*

Kampala is the capital of which country?

355 *Natural History*

Which small rodent gets its common name from the French word meaning 'to sleep'?

356 *Nature*

Published by the World Conservation Union, what are catalogued in the Red Lists?

357 *Monopoly*

In Monopoly, what happens to a player who throws doubles three times in succession?

358 *Pop Music Magazines*

What do the initials *NME* stand for?

359 *Physiology*
What, in the human body, is the CNS?

360 *Phrases and Sayings*
According to the expression, to which city are people sent when they are being cold-shouldered?

361 *Inventions*
For the pioneering of what is the Scotsman John Logie Baird best remembered?

362 *Astronomy*
Which Italian astronomer was sentenced to imprisonment in 1633 for his support of Copernicus's theories?

363 *Nursery Rhymes*
What, in a nursery rhyme, did Lucy Locket lose?

364 *The UK*
Chelmsford is the administrative centre for which county?

365 *Food and Drink*
What are the two main ingredients of Cockieleekie soup?

366 *Physics*
9.806 metres per second is the internationally adopted value of acceleration due to what force?

367 *The Calendar*
What name is given to the period in the Christian calendar that covers the four Sundays leading up to Christmas?

368 *Travel in the UK*
Apex, SuperApex, SuperSaver and Network AwayBreak are all types of what?

369 *Religion*
Salem is the Old Testament name for which city?

370 *Organizations*
What is the name of the human rights organization established in the UK in 1961 to campaign for, amongst other things, the release of prisoners of conscience worldwide?

371 *Tennis*
The American sisters Venus and Serena: what is their surname?

372 *The USA*

The name of only one of the states begins with the letter P. Which state?

373 *The USA*

Which city is the largest in the state of Nevada, and a world-famous gambling and entertainment centre?

374 *Mythology*

Which god, in Norse mythology, was drawn across the sky by goats pulling a wagon that rattled and caused thunder?

375 *National Anthems*

Which country is described in its national anthem as: 'The land of the free and the home of the brave'?

376 *Literature*

In which Jules Verne novel is Captain Nemo the commander of the submarine *Nautilus*?

377 *Mythology*

Who killed the Minotaur in the labyrinth?

378 *Literature*

The son of a country squire is sent to public school where he finds himself at the mercy of a bullying older boy called Flashman. In which novel?

379 *The Cold War*

The USA's Strategic Defense Initiative took its nickname from the title of a popular George Lucas film. Which film?

380 *Television*

Seymour Skinner is the school principal in which cartoon series?

381 *Travel in the UK*

What type of services are Sally, Brittany, Stena Line and P&O?

382 *Television*

Which comedian's early characterizations included the kebab shop owner Stavros and the plasterer Loadsamoney?

383 *Geography*

What is the largest island in the Mediterranean Sea?

384 *Africa*

On which river is the Kariba Dam?

385 *Europe*

After the Vatican, and with an area of 1.9 square kilometres, which European principality is the smallest independent state in the world?

386 *Currency*

In which year in the 1970s was decimal currency introduced in the United Kingdom?

387 *Measures*

The capacity of one standard teaspoon is 5 millilitres. What is the capacity of one standard tablespoon?

388 *Latin Phrases*

As seen on tombstones, what is the literal meaning of the Latin phrase *Hic jacet*?

389 *Commonwealth*

Which is the only country to have left the Commonwealth and not to have rejoined it?

390 *Geography*

Of which African country is Dakar the capital city?

391 *Proverbs*

According to the saying, what can you not make from a sow's ear?

392 *The USA*

Brooklyn Bridge, Manhattan Bridge, Williamsburg Bridge and Queensboro Bridge: over which river do they all stand?

393 *British Cities*

Gillygate, Stonegate, Fossgate, Coppergate and Ousegate are main thoroughfares in the centre of which English city?

394 *Modern Literature*

Which twentieth-century novel introduced the concepts of 'Big Brother', 'the Thought Police' and 'Doublethink'?

395 *The Bible*

In which book of the Bible does the presentation of the Ten Commandments to Moses occur?

396 *Religion*

Over 80 per cent of the population of India follows which religion?

397 *Astronomy*

Which constellation in the heavens is named after a pair of mythological twins?

398 *Geography*

The five African countries with a Mediterranean coastline all share which official language?

399 *Dickens' London*

Which London prison, which closed in 1842, is featured in Charles Dickens' novel *Little Dorrit?*

400 *Politics*

Muhammed Ali Jinnah was the first governor-general of which country, on its creation in 1947?

401 *Classical Music*

Whose Eighth Symphony is known as the 'Symphony of a Thousand' owing to the large number of performers it requires?

402 *World Religion*

In which religion is the place of worship known as the gurdwara?

403 *Sport*

The West Indian cricketer Brian Lara is a native of which country?

404 *Ancient History*

In which modern-day country did the ancient people the Etruscans live?

405 *Literature*

Who created the fictional town of Middlemarch?

406 *Children's Literature*

In *The Wonderful Wizard of Oz* the Lion wants courage and the Tin Man wants a heart. What does the Scarecrow want?

407 *The British Monarchy*

Who was the first Hanoverian monarch of Great Britain?

408 *Literature*

In which novel by Jane Austen does the eponymous heroine have the surname Woodhouse?

409 *Rowing*

In coxed fours and coxed eights, what term describes the oarsman who sits immediately in front of the cox?

410 *The Arts*

In which field of the arts are Adrian Noble, Terry Hands and Deborah Warner well-known names?

411 *Horse Racing*

At which racecourse in Paris is the Prix de L'Arc de Triomphe run?

412 *Rugby Union*

When England play Scotland in the Six Nations tournament, which trophy, inaugurated in 1879, is also at stake?

413 *Horse Racing*

Which of the five English classics is run at Epsom in the same week as the Derby?

414 *The UK*

Milton Keynes, Aylesbury and High Wycombe are the largest towns in which English county?

415 *Board Games*

What is the name of the world conquest board game, in which players attack and counter-attack one another in 42 countries on six continents?

416 *Sport in the 1990s*

Which jockey rode a record seven consecutive winners at a single meeting at Ascot in September 1996?

417 *Words*

Which word from Hindi, meaning one who is learned in the Sanskrit disciplines, is now commonly given to a person who is an authority on a particular subject?

418 *History of Sport*

In which annual event, founded in 1829, was Susan Brown the first woman to take part, in 1981?

419 *Australia*

Which medical rescue service has its headquarters at Broken Hill, New South Wales?

420 Chemistry

What term is used to indicate how many protons are contained in the nucleus of an atom of any element?

421 Europe

What is the official language of the principality of Andorra?

422 Historical Figures

In 1532, he resigned as Lord Chancellor, in 1534, he refused to assent under oath to the Act of Succession and in 1535, he was executed. Who was he?

423 Geography

In which ocean is the Java Trench, over 25,000 feet in depth?

424 Transport

What is the name of the Carlisle-based haulier, with distinctive red, green and gold lorries, each of which has a girl's name?

425 Ships and the Sea

In which year was the *Titanic* launched?

426 Science

Chlorophyll is the green pigment found in plants. What colour is the pigment xanthophyll?

427 Shakespeare

In which play is Imogen the daughter of the King of Britain?

428 Computers

In computer terminology, for what does the abbreviation DMA stand?

429 London

In which London borough are Twickenham rugby football ground and the Royal Botanic Gardens at Kew?

430 Nobel Prizes

How many Nobel prizes are available to be awarded every year?

431 Literature

Who was in Bedford jail in the seventeenth century when he began writing the work for which he is now best remembered?

432 *The UK*

Which National Park lies wholly in Cumbria?

433 *Finance*

Futures in coffee, cocoa, wheat, barley and potatoes are traded at the LCE in London. What is the LCE?

434 *Literature*

How, in the title of a John Fowles' novel, later a film starring Meryl Streep, is the character Sarah Woodruff described?

435 *Sport*

What connects Interlagos in Brazil, Hockenheim in Germany, Monza in Italy and Imola in San Marino?

436 *Business and Commerce*

What sort of companies are Earl Shilton, Nottingham Imperial and Kent Reliance?

437 *Proverbs*

'Necessity is the mother of...' what?

438 *The United Nations*

Which organ of the United Nations has the major responsibility for peace keeping?

439 *Mythology*

Artemis was the Greek goddess of the hunt. Who is her Roman equivalent?

440 *Towns*

Uppsala, Malmo and Helsingborg are towns in which European country?

441 *Charles Dickens*

Which eponymous hero of a Dickens novel has a pet raven called Grip?

442 *People*

For his translation of what, in the sixteenth century, is Miles Coverdale remembered?

443 *Religion*

The election of a pope is signified by white smoke emerging from a chimney in the Vatican city. What causes the smoke?

444 *Geography*

What is the capital of Morocco?

445 *Proverbs*

'Beauty is potent but money is…' what?

446 *London*

What, in London, are the Whitechapel, the Courtauld and the Hayward?

447 *Roman History*

Which Roman Emperor rebuilt Byzantium as his capital and renamed it after himself?

448 *Charity*

By what acronym is the Royal Society for Mentally Handicapped Children and Adults better known?

449 *Charity*

Which charity was founded by Miss Eglantine Jebb in 1919 after seeing the plight of children in the Balkans?

450 *Sport*

Which major international sporting event will be staged in Manchester in 2002?

15 to 1

ROUND TWO
Questions

451 *Food and Drink*

In a dish served 'Florentine', which vegetable will be an ingredient?

452 *Medicine*

Factor Eight is used in the treatment of disorders of…?

453 *Shakespeare*

Sir John Falstaff decides to pay court to Mistress Page and Mistress Ford, hoping thereby to obtain some money, as they have charge of their husbands' purses. In which Shakespeare play?

454 *The Bible*

To whom did St Paul address the first Epistle in the New Testament?

455 *Business*

Manheim auctions in the United States is the biggest of its kind in the world. What are sold there?

456 *History*

Which religious service is set out in the fourteenth-century book the *Liber Regalis*?

457 *Geography*

Lake Maggiore lies on the border of which two countries?

458 *Geography*

Newark-on-Trent, Mansfield and Sutton-in-Ashfield are towns in which county?

459 *The Queen*

What is the Queen's second Christian name?

460 *Languages*

Wade Giles and Pinyin are two systems of a phonetic alphabet for which language?

461 *Football*

Which English Premiership club play their home matches at White Hart Lane?

462 *Ancient History*

Ankhesenamen was the Queen of which Egyptian pharaoh?

463 *Geography*

The northern coastal region of which continent was formerly known as the 'Barbary States'?

464 *The UK*

Humbly Grove and Stockbridge in Hampshire, Palmers Wood in Surrey, Welton in Lincolnshire. What is the connection?

465 *Religion/History*

Lindisfarne monastery, on Holy Island off the coast of Northumberland, was founded by which seventh-century Irish monk?

466 *The Media*

Which voluntary body replaced the Press Council in 1991 and operates the self-regulation system of the newspaper and magazine industry?

467 *Politics*

In a proportional representation system of voting, what does the abbreviation STV stand for?

468 *Literature*

In Charles Kingsley's *The Water Babies* there are two memorable governess characters. Mrs Do-as-you-would-be-done-by is one, what is the name of the other?

469 *History*

Which two countries fought the Bishops' Wars of 1639 and 1640?

470 *Opera*

What is Madame Butterfly's Japanese name?

471 *Greek Mythology*

What is the collective name of the three daughters of Zeus embodying beauty and social accomplishments?

472 *Business*

What is the name for the point at which the income from sales covers the cost of production, with neither profit nor loss being made?

473 *Architecture*

What sort of structure, usually built in an elevated position, takes its name from the Italian for 'beautiful view'?

474 *Army Nicknames*

American soldiers used be known as GIs. What does GI stand for?

475 *London Landmarks*

A statue of which twelfth-century English king, on horseback with a sword in his raised right hand, stands outside the Houses of Parliament in Old Palace Yard?

476 *History of Science*

In 1774, the British chemist Joseph Priestly isolated a gas which he called 'dephlogisticated air'. It was later renamed by his French rival Antoine Lavoisier. How was it renamed?

477 *Classic Films*

Which classic film of the 1940s, starring Trevor Howard and Celia Johnson, is the story of a love affair that begins with a chance meeting between a local doctor and a suburban housewife at a railway station?

478 *Famous Battles*

Afflavit Deus et dissipantur, meaning 'God blew, and they are dispersed', was an inscription on Elizabeth I's medal awarded to those who fought against which foreign fleet?

479 *Anniversaries/Space Exploration*

20 July 1999 was the 30th anniversary of which famous event in space exploration history?

480 *Government*

1 Carlton Gardens, SW1, is the official London residence of the holder of which Cabinet post?

481 *South Africa*

Cape Town is the legislative capital, Bloemfontein is the judicial capital, so which city is the executive or administrative capital?

482 *Food and Drink*

The name of which Spanish rice dish, made from chicken, shellfish and vegetables, is derived from the pan in which it is cooked and served?

483 *Music*

In a Gilbert and Sullivan opera, the profession of the character John Wellington Wells is also the title of the opera. Which one?

484 Science

What is the name for the unit of pressure equal to 60 millimetres of mercury?

485 Politics

In how many general elections did Harold Wilson lead the Labour Party?

486 International Organizations

With its headquarters in Addis Ababa, what is the OAU?

487 Technology and Warfare

What kind of missile is one described as a SAM?

488 Medieval Outlaws

What is the name of the eleventh-century Anglo-Saxon rebel, who defended the Isle of Ely against the Normans and was the subject of a novel by Charles Kingsley, published in 1866?

489 Geography

What is the capital of Nepal?

490 Nineteenth-century Literature

Elinor Dashwood is in love with Edward Ferrers and conceals her distress at learning that he is secretly engaged to Lucy Steele – news which causes him to be disinherited in favour of his brother: in which novel by Jane Austen?

491 Annual Events in the UK

The Furry Dance Festival at Helston in Cornwall, the International Highland Games at Blair Atholl and the Chelsea Flower Show: in which month do these events take place?

492 English Law

What term is usually used in law to refer to evidence that confirms and supports other evidence that has already been given?

493 Politics

There are three treasury ministers in the Cabinet: the Prime Minister, the Chancellor of the Exchequer and which other post?

494 *Children's Literature*

Who is the medical practitioner from Puddleby-on-the-Marsh who is taught to speak to animals by his parrot Polynesia?

495 *History of the United Nations*

What nationality was U Thant, Secretary General of the UN from 1961 to 1971?

496 *Science*

What is the name of the mineral hardness scale on which talc registers 1, and diamond registers 10?

497 *The UK*

What is the name of the famous castle, 12 miles north of Dundee, believed to be the setting for Shakespeare's *Macbeth* and the home of the Lyons family (later Bowes-Lyon), the family of the Queen Mother, since 1372?

498 *Art*

Red Vineyard at Arles is the only one of his paintings sold during the lifetime of which artist?

499 *The Bible*

On which day, numerically, did God create the sun, moon and stars?

500 *Language*

What sort of error is a parachronism?

501 *Charles Dickens*

'It was the best of times, it was the worst of times, it was the age of wisdom, it was the age of foolishness'. These are the opening lines of which novel?

502 *Law*

What name is given to the six divisions into which England and Wales are divided for legal purposes?

503 *Language*

In shallah in Arabic, *deo volente* in Latin, both mean what, in English?

504 *Poetry*

Which month, according to the first line of T.S. Eliot's poem 'The Waste Land', is the cruellest month?

505 *Food and Drink*

Which famous cocktail is made with pineapple juice, rum and coconut milk?

506 *Musicals*

'Cool', 'A Boy Like That', 'Gee Officer Krupke!': hit numbers from which Leonard Bernstein/Stephen Sondheim musical?

507 *Famous Names in Sport*

Sir John Sholto Douglas, Marquess of Queensbury, sponsored the Queensbury Rules. These form the basis of the rules of which sport?

508 *Associations*

The National Association of Licensed Door Supervisors was formed in 1996 to improve the image of the 'profession'. By what name are these 'professionals' more commonly known?

509 *Pressure Groups*

With what is the pressure group NACRO concerned?

510 *The Royal Family*

What relation is Princess Margaret to Princess Alexandra?

511 *The UK*

Leigh Delamere Services (on the M4), Marlborough College and the market town on Chippenham are in which county?

512 *Literature*

The Three Musketeers, by Alexandre Dumas: what were the names of the musketeers?

513 *Music*

The Italian musical term 'parlando' indicates that the piece is to be sung in what manner?

514 *Fictional Characters*

What's the name of Sherlock Holmes' much cleverer brother, who works for a government department?

515 *Africa*

What are the names of the two ethnic groups that comprise most of the population of Rwanda and Burundi?

516 *Words*

Hyalography is the art of writing or engraving on what substance or surface?

517 *Customs*

On entering the UK at ports and airports, there are three colour-coded channels: one for nothing to declare, one for travellers from an EU country, and one for travellers from a non-EU country with something to declare. What are the three colours?

518 *Personal Finance*

If someone invests £100 for three years at 10 per cent per annum and receives a total of £130, what sort of interest would they be earning?

519 *The Olympics*

Chris Finnegan in 1968 was the last British representative to win an Olympic gold medal in which sport?

520 *Chemistry*

Brass is principally an alloy of which two metals?

521 *History of Sport*

What is the Cornish-born Fitzsimmon's place in the history of sport?

522 *Twentieth-century Literature*

Which novel by J.D. Salinger is narrated by a 16-year-old boy, a boarder at an expensive prep school called Pencey, which he leaves to go to New York City?

523 *The USA*

What are Logan in Boston, Dulles in Washington and Hartsfield in Atlanta?

524 *Musicals*

'My Favourite Things', 'Climb Ev'ry Mountain' and 'The Lonely Goatherd': hit numbers from which Rodgers and Hammerstein musical?

525 *Transport in London*

What is the DLR?

526 *Latin Phrases*

What does the Latin phrase *De die in diem* mean?

527 *The British Monarchy*

Who was the last British monarch not to have been married throughout his reign?

528 *British Heroes*

During the American War of Independence, Admiral Lord Richard commanded the British sea forces, while his brother, Sir William, commanded the land forces. What is their family name?

529 *History of the Twentieth Century*

In which war was the Gulf of Tonkin incident a major event in 1964?

530 *Politics*

Which nineteenth-century British prime minister took the title Earl of Beaconsfield when he went to the House of Lords?

531 *The UK*

The UK's spying agency, MI6, is also known as the SIS. What does SIS stand for?

532 *The Bible*

Which insect in the Book of Proverbs is given as an example of industriousness to the sluggard?

533 *Popular Expressions*

According to an apocryphal story, the long nose and inquisitive nature of which sixteenth-century Archbishop of Canterbury gave rise to the expression 'nosey Parker'?

534 *Aviation*

In relation to aeroplanes, what does the abbreviation C-of-A stand for?

535 *Famous Houses*

Broadlands, near Southampton, was the home of which British naval commander and statesman, who died in 1979?

536 *Art*

The works of which Belgian surrealist (who died in the 1960s) often feature mysterious men in bowler hats?

537 *Literature*

Who was the author of *King Solomon's Mines* (1885) and *Allan Quartermain* (1887)?

538 *European History*

The War of the Spanish Succession and the War of the Austrian Succession took place in the first half of which century?

539 *Chemistry*

What term is used to describe the movement of a liquid through a semi-permeable membrane, from a less concentrated solution to a more concentrated one?

540 *Twentieth-century Literature*

In which Tennessee Williams play are Blanche Dubois, her sister Stella and brother-in-law Stanley Kowalski leading characters?

541 *Famous Criminals*

Hawley Harvey were the first names of which infamous murderer, who in 1910 became the first criminal to be captured by the use of radio?

542 *Ships and the Sea*

What, in the context of ships and the sea, is meant by the word 'jury'?

543 *Food and Drink*

A raw egg swallowed whole in sherry and Worcester sauce: how is this hangover cure better known?

544 *Beatrix Potter*

An unnamed tailor makes a coat for the mayor's Christmas wedding, with the help of some mice, whom the old man had saved from his cat. Which Beatrix Potter tale is this?

545 *Transport*

A slate rip, foam aspirators and BA sets are carried on which specific type of vehicle?

546 *Painting*

Which Dutch artist of the sixteenth and seventeenth centuries painted *The Merry Toper*, *The Merry Company* and, most famously, *The Laughing Cavalier*?

547 *British History*

Which British prime minister in the 1920s served the shortest term this century – just 209 days?

548 *Food and Drink*

Orange Pekoe is a variety of what?

549 *Currencies*

The forint, comprising 100 fillur, is the main unit of currency of which European country?

550 *Twentieth-century Literature*

Junkie (1953), *Nova Express* (1964) and *Cities of the Red Night* (1981) are by which innovative American author?

551 *Peerage*

Campbell is the family name of which Scottish Duke?

552 *Football Club Nicknames*

Sheffield Wednesday are the Owls, Millwall are the Lions, what are Leicester City?

553 *Science*

Which unit of weight is used to measure the fineness of woven materials (such as nylon), equal to 1 gram per 9000 metres?

554 *English Battles*

The battle of Sedgemoor in 1685 was the last to be fought on English soil. It occurred during which uprising?

555 *Flowers*

The name of which evergreen climbing plant is derived from its distinctive flowers that have parts which supposedly resemble aspects of the Crucifixion?

556 *Astronomy*

The Great Red Spot is a prominent feature of which planet in our solar system?

557 *Medicine*

A sphygmomanometer is used in the measurement of what?

558 *Sport*

A yokozuna is a grand champion of which sport?

559 *Alphabets*

Which letter is represented in Braille by a single raised dot, and in Morse Code by dot-dash?

560 *Science*

What name is given to the force experienced by pilots when their plane accelerates or decelerates rapidly?

561 *Religion*

In the western Christian calendar, what name is given to the Thursday after Trinity Sunday?

562 *Shakespeare*

In *Romeo and Juliet*, Romeo dies by taking poison. How does Juliet kill herself?

563 *The Royal Family*

The Union Jack is flown over government buildings on 20 November of each year to celebrate what?

564 *Geography*

Ashby-de-la-Zouch, Ibstock and Uppingham are all in which county?

565 *Law*

What is meant by the Latin expression *mens rea*?

566 *Fish*

To which family does the goldfish belong?

567 *Charles Dickens*

Against whom, in a Dickens novel, does Mrs Bardell bring an action for breach of promise?

568 *Twentieth-century History*

Nancy Astor was the first woman MP to sit in the House of Commons. Which constituency did she represent?

569 *British Newspapers*

The Tablet is a weekly periodical of which denomination of the Christian church?

570 *London Landmarks*

The Arts Centre on the South Bank was built around which building – the only one remaining from the Festival of Britain in 1951?

571 *Famous Couples*

Who is the famous wife of the Italian film producer Carlo Ponti?

572 *The UK*

Kimbolton Castle, the Cromwell Museum and Ely Cathedral are in which English county?

573 *Oscar Wilde*

What was the name of the imaginary invalid friend invented by Algernon Moncrieff in *The Importance of Being Earnest*?

574 *Wine*

What word describes a wine made from the produce of a single year?

575 *Political History*

In 1924 and 1929, the Labour Party formed minority governments. Who, on both occasions, was the Prime Minister?

576 *Ancient History*

Which famous pair of lovers were defeated at the Battle of Actium by Octavian in 31 BC?

577 *Science*

A phon is a unit for the measurement of what?

578 *International Law*

The Hague Conventions, signed between 1899 and 1907, concern the conduct of the law under which circumstances?

579 *The USA*

Which US state was named after the wife of Charles I?

580 *Poetry*

'God's in his heaven/All's right with the world'. Which poet wrote these famous words?

581 *Classical Music*

The violin concertos nicknamed 'Il Sospetto', the 'Storm at Sea' and 'Il Favorito' are the work of which composer?

582 *Musicals*

What is the title of the stage and film musical, which starred Jane Russell and Marilyn Monroe, in which the lead character is the diamond-loving Lorelei Lee?

583 Human Anatomy

In humans, which part of the foot is the hallux?

584 British History

What name was given to the conspiracy of 1683 by English Whig extremists intent on murdering Charles II and his brother, the future James II?

585 Classical Music

Which piece by Saint-Saëns is based on a poem in which Death, the fiddler, summons skeletons from their graves at midnight?

586 Parliament

The holder of which office is the Speaker's principal adviser in all matters of procedure, and sits at the Table of the House during sittings?

587 The UK

What name is given to houses and apartments that are in the gift of the monarch, for example those at Hampton Court or St James's Palace?

588 The Bible

What name is given in the Bible to someone who prepared perfumes and spices?

589 Nursery Rhymes

Who killed Cock Robin?

590 Art

What is the name of the abstract art form originated by Picasso and Braque in the early 1900s?

591 Nineteenth-century Literature

In which Charlotte Brontë novel does the eponymous heroine and narrator confide that 'Reader, I married him'?

592 Sunday Newspapers

Which Sunday newspaper has separate sections called 'Culture', 'Style' and a magazine section called The Sunday Magazine?

593 The British Monarchy

Edward IV was the first, and Richard III the last monarch of which royal house?

594 *Politics*

Only two leaders of the Conservative Party in the twentieth century have not also been Prime Minister: William Hague and who in the early 1920s?

595 *US Presidents*

Warren Harding, Calvin Coolidge and Herbert Hoover were all US Presidents during which decade?

596 *Martial Arts*

What is the name of the Japanese martial art, derived from samurai sword fighting, in which combatants use bamboo staffs or wooden swords to deliver blows?

597 *History of Athletics*

What is the name of the British athlete who, in 1994, became the first woman to complete a full set of championship titles, when she won the European 400-metre hurdles final in Helsinki, to add to her Olympic, World and Commonwealth titles?

598 *Comic Verse*

'The stately homes of England/How beautiful they stand/To prove the upper classes/Have still the upper hand.' Who wrote these words?

599 *Physics*

Which imperial unit of measurement is equivalent to 25.4 millimetres?

600 *Literature*

In which profession did Somerset Maugham qualify, in the same year in which his first novel, *Liza of Lambeth*, was published?

601 *The Nineteenth Century*

What is the title of the three-volume work by Karl Marx which appeals for a classless society where rewards are shared equally?

602 *History of Astronomy*

What specific and connected contribution to astronomy was made by William Herschel in 1781, Johann Galle in 1846 and Clyde Tombaugh in 1930?

603 *Parliament*

Under which act of Parliament of 1707 were England and Scotland united under the name Great Britain?

604 *Business*

What is the name of the American agent and impresario who founded International Management Group, and whose clients have included Arnold Palmer, Jackie Stewart and Nick Faldo?

605 *Opera*

The courage of a faithful wife saves her husband from execution at the hands of a Spanish oppressor: this is the theme of whose only opera?

606 *Medicine*

A hepatologist is a physician specializing in diseases of which organ of the body?

607 *Inventions*

Which aid to musicians was invented by Dietrich Winkel, and patented by a German, Johan Maelzel, in 1816?

608 *Social Welfare in the Nineteenth Century*

Where in the Wirral did the Victorian soap-maker, William Hesketh Lever, found his factory in 1888, building a garden village beside it to house the workers?

609 *Famous Entertainers*

Born Frederick Austerlitz in Omaha, Nebraska in 1899, he starred in *Top Hat* in the 1930s, *Easter Parade* in the 1940s and *Funny Face* in the 1950s. By what name is he better known?

610 *History*

What is the name of the series of defensive fortifications built between 1929 and 1932 along France's eastern border with Germany?

611 *Education*

Which institution was established in the UK in 1969 to enable mature students, without any qualifications, to study to degree level without regular attendance?

612 *Contemporary Literature*

The highly acclaimed work by Frank McCourt called *Angela's Ashes*, published in 1996 and released in the cinema in 2000, is a poignant tale of growing up in the slums. In which country is it set?

613 *National Collections*

Located in Kew, Surrey, the PRO contains collections of legal, governmental and historical documents. What do the initials PRO stand for?

614 *Irish Politics*

Which political party was founded by Eamon de Valera in 1926?

615 *Film Directors*

Life is Sweet, *Naked* and *Secrets and Lies* are films made in the 1990s by which award-winning British director?

616 *Domestic Animals*

Cornish, Rhode Island Red and Leghorn are breeds of which bird?

617 *Legal Terms*

Which two-word French term, meaning coercion or irresistible compulsion, is used in commercial contracts to describe events that are outside the control of the parties involved?

618 *Computer Technology*

In order to log on to the World Wide Web, you need an ISP. What does ISP stand for?

619 *Sport and Games*

In the game of billiards, each player has a white ball and there is also a red ball on the table. How do they distinguish between the two white balls?

620 *Shakespeare*

Who, in a Shakespeare play, utters these famous words: 'Friends, Romans, countrymen... lend me your ears'?

621 *Medicine*

What name is given to the pressure wave in a blood vessel that corresponds to the heart beat?

622 *Chemistry*

What name is given to a substance that speeds up or slows down the rate of a chemical reaction, but which itself undergoes no permanent change?

623 *Counties*

Hampshire has a border with five other counties. Name two of the five.

624 *History*

Which king did Robert Catesby and Guy Fawkes intend to kill by placing barrels of gunpowder below the Houses of Parliament?

625 *History*

In which country did the Romanov dynasty rule from 1613 until 1917?

626 *Olympics*

Only two track events for men are run in a straight line: the 100 metres and which other?

627 *Science*

An ERG is a unit of what?

628 *Language*

What does the prefix 'poly' mean?

629 *Mathematics*

What term is used for the result of multiplying two or more numbers?

630 *Quotations*

Which member of the royal family once famously said: 'When I appear in public, people expect me to neigh, grind my teeth, paw the ground and swish my tail — none of which is easy'?

631 *Chemistry*

Which element is present in all acids?

632 *Children's Literature*

Who, in a famous children's story by Lewis Carroll, meets the characters Tweedledum and Tweedledee?

633 *Economics*

What term is given to the persistent increase in the general level of prices?

634 *Food and Drink*

What is the main basis of bouillabaisse?

635 *Mathematics*

On which number is the duodecimal number system based?

636 *Mottos*

What is the Latin for 'never despair'?

637 *Pop Music*

Which major rock star got his stage name because he used to wear a striped jumper that made him look like a wasp?

638 *Botany*

What adjective describes trees that are cone-bearing?

639 *Trade Names*

The name of which Swedish motor car manufacturing company is derived from the Latin for 'I roll'?

640 *Classical Literature*

Who wrote the epic *The Aeneid*?

641 *Philosophy*

What term is used to describe someone who denies the existence of a God?

642 *Great Slogans in Sport*

In golf, Arnie's Army were supporters of Arnold Palmer. Who do Tiger's Troopers follow?

643 *London*

Which building is the official residence of the Lord Mayor of London?

644 *Mathematics*

What is 1 to the power of 10?

645 *Religion*

Which religious group, founded in 1865 in London, has a world leader known as the General?

646 *Airlines*

What is the name of Spain's national airline?

647 *Cricket*

What name is given to an over in which no runs are scored off the bat?

648 *History of Television*

In which classic television series, first shown in the 1960s, were Bob Ferris and Terry Collier the chief characters?

649 *Film*

Which Walt Disney film of 1967 features the songs 'Bare Necessities', 'I Wanna Be Like You' and 'Trust in Me'?

650 *Human Anatomy*

Where in the human body are bones called carpi, metacarpi and phalanges?

651 *Language*

Often used in crossword puzzles, what name is given to a word formed by transposing the letters of another word?

652 *Chemical Symbols*

K is the symbol for which chemical element?

653 *Motorways*

The M56, the M63, the M66, the M67 and the M602 all serve which northern city?

654 *Sport*

With which sport do you associate The Aqueduct in New York, Santa Anita in Los Angeles and Churchill Downs in Louisville, Kentucky?

655 *Olympic Athletics*

The men's multi-discipline event is the decathlon. What is the women's multi-discipline event called?

656 *Archaeology*

For what event, in 1922, are Lord Carnarvon and Howard Carter best remembered?

657 *First Lines*

'Oh! say, can you see, by the dawn's early light' is the first line of what?

658 *The English Monarchy*

The House of Normandy reigned in England during which two centuries?

659 *Music*

What word describes a note that is neither flat nor sharp?

660　*European History*

The war from 1853–1856 was known to contemporaries as the Russian War. What is it known as today?

661　*The UK*

Which government department is responsible for immigration control, the prison services and fire services?

662　*Physics*

The centigrade scale is now usually referred to by the name of the man who devised it. What was his name?

663　*Words*

Which French phrase is used to describe an author's assumed name or pen name?

664　*Geography*

Canada, Brazil, Morocco and Portugal all have coastlines on which ocean?

665　*Sport*

In which sport would a 'night watchman' play a role?

666　*Asian Geography*

What in Asia is the Hindu Kush?

667　*Architecture*

Fenestration describes the arrangement of what in a building?

668　*Sport*

In cricket what is meant by the umpire raising both hands high above his head?

669　*Science*

Which part of an electric lightbulb transmits light by becoming white hot?

670　*Birds*

What name is generally given to birds of the genus *Cygnus*?

671　*Food and Drink*

What is the name of the Spanish soup, served cold and made from tomatoes, peppers, cucumber, garlic, onion and croutons?

672　*Museums*

In which city in Austria is the Mozart Birthplace Museum?

673 *Television*

Who played a character called
Dr Edward Fitzgerald, otherwise
known as Fitz?

674 *Folktales*

How did Scheherezade keep her
new husband entertained at
night, and thus ensure her safety?

675 *The Bible*

Uriah the Hittite was her first
husband, King David her
second. Who was she?

676 *Ancient History*

Which of the Seven Wonders of
the World was built at Ephesus
in 356BC?

677 *The USA*

What do Larry King, Jay Leno
and David Letterman do on
American television?

678 *Television*

In which award-winning
BBC comedy series did the two
leading zany female characters
have the surnames Monsoon
and Stone?

679 *Musicals*

Which Lionel Bart musical,
based on a nineteenth-century
novel, opens at feeding time in
a workhouse?

680 *Food and Drink*

Cassis is a syrup made from
which fruit?

681 *People*

Who would live in a residence
called a 'manse'?

682 *History*

Which period in history meaning
'New Stone Age' followed the
Mesolithic Period, or Middle
Stone Age?

683 *Computing*

Beginner's All-Purpose Symbolic
Instruction Code is a high-level
programming language. By what
acronym is it better known?

684 *Ballet*

In which ballet, with music by
Tchaikovsky, is Princess Odette
turned into a bird by the
magician von Rothbart?

685 *Commonwealth*

Which is the only Commonwealth country to have both an Atlantic and Pacific coastline?

686 *Roman Mythology*

What was Pax the Roman goddess of?

687 *Counties*

Cambridgeshire lies to the west of Suffolk. Which counties lie to the north and south of Suffolk?

688 *Anatomy*

What is the medical name for the thigh bone?

689 *Astronomy*

Which planet is named after the Roman messenger of the gods?

690 *British History*

What name is given to the project that caused disastrous speculation fever in 1720?

691 *History and Shakespeare*

After defeat by Mark Antony at Philippi, how did Brutus die?

692 *Greek Mythology*

King Priam was the last king of which city?

693 *Religion*

At which Jewish festival, celebrated in the month of Nisan, is unleavened bread traditionally eaten?

694 *Architecture*

Which building is described in Brewer's *Twentieth Century Phrase and Fable* dictionary as 'Undoubtedly the best-known building in Australia'?

695 *The UK*

On which river do Shrewsbury, Worcester and Gloucester all stand?

696 *The Arts*

What is the Academy of St Martin's in the Fields?

697 *English Literature*

Which novel by George Eliot is the tale of a linen weaver, living in a country village during the Industrial Revolution?

698 *Civil Aviation*

In which Commonwealth country are there airports with the codes CCU, BOM and DEL?

699 *History*

What was the name of the faithful gillie to Queen Victoria, played by Billy Connolly in a film?

700 *Philosophy*

What name is given to the branch of philosophy that deals with principles of reasoning?

701 *Legend*

What name is given to the chalice used by Christ at the Last Supper which became the subject of medieval legend and romance?

702 *Language*

Israel has two official languages: Hebrew and what else?

703 *Theatre*

Inspector Javert and Jean Valjean are leading characters in which long-running musical in London's West End?

704 *The Bible*

Who in the New Testament was the son of Zacharias and Elizabeth, and through his mother's line, a cousin of Jesus?

705 *Law*

In which country does the Court of Justice of the European Communities sit?

706 *Physics*

What is defined as the product of a moving body's mass and velocity?

707 *Marine Biology*

Which species of whale is the largest living animal?

708 *The History of Medicine*

Whose method of treating surgical wounds using carbolic acid to prevent septic infection revolutionized modern surgery?

709 *Musical Theatre*

What is the title of the Rodgers and Hammerstein musical about cowboys and farmers in the Midwest?

710 *Language*

What is the literal translation of the German word 'kindergarten'?

711 *Chess*

The opening move can be made by either a pawn or which other piece?

712 *Sport*

'About', 'bear away', 'luff', 'gybe' and 'tack' are all common terms in which sport?

713 *Music*

What does the term 'diminuendo' mean?

714 *History*

The ancient Egyptians wrote on papyrus, made from stems of the papyrus plant. This was replaced gradually by parchment. What was parchment made from?

715 *Medicine*

Which, now common, device was invented in 1958 by the Swedish doctor Ake Senning and used to regulate the heartbeat?

716 *London*

In which London street is there a famous 'Hospital for Sick Children'?

717 *European Landmarks*

What is the name of the statue, based on a character created by Hans Christian Andersen, which sits in the harbour at Copenhagen?

718 *Geography*

What do the French call the English Channel?

719 *Shakespeare*

The ghost of which Scottish nobleman appears at a banquet given by Macbeth?

720 *Geography*

Which sea separates Egypt, Sudan and Eritrea from the Arabian Peninsula?

721 *The UK*

Which two famous points in the UK are 603 miles apart, as the crow flies, and approximately 900 miles by road?

722 *London*

Each child at St Clement Danes Primary School in London is given two pieces of fruit following an annual service at St Clement Danes Church. Which two fruits are given?

723 *Shakespeare*

The throne of which country, in a Shakespeare play, is inherited by the Prince of Norway after the heir to the throne is killed by a poisoned sword?

724 *Rugby Union*

What name is given to the touring team from the British Isles, which includes players from England, Ireland, Scotland and Wales?

725 *Ancient Greece*

Which poison did Socrates take to die?

726 *Physics*

The rate of change of velocity, expressed in metres or feet per second squared, is known as what?

727 *The USA*

On the East Coast it is New York; which US city has the largest population on the West Coast?

728 *Television*

Which ITV company is based in Belfast?

729 *Poetry*

The first line of 'The Soldier' is 'If I should die, think only this of me.' Who wrote this poem?

730 *Computing*

The 'Lisa' and, more recently, the 'Macintosh', are personal computers developed by which company?

731 *The Animal World*

What name is given to the class of vertebrates that includes frogs, toads and newts?

732 *Computing*

What medical term describes a programme that attaches itself to a file within a computer and corrupts the data each time the file is run?

733 *Geography*

What is the capital of Romania?

734 *Shakespeare*

In *Othello*, what emotion does Iago describe as the 'green-eyed monster'?

735 *Musicals*

In which Lerner and Loewe musical are the main characters a professor, a flower seller and a dustman?

736 *Classical Mythology*

Who was the Queen of the Amazons whose girdle Heracles stole, who also featured in Shakespeare's *A Midsummer Night's Dream*?

737 *Books*

John Grey's book on the differences between men and women is called *Men are from Mars, Women are from…* where?

738 *Politics*

Perry Barr, Selly Oak and Edgbaston are parliamentary constituencies in which city?

739 *Airports*

The airport at Dyce serves which Scottish city?

740 *Radio Communications*

Which radio code word, a man's name, is used in radio communications to mean 'understood'?

741 *Pop Bands*

How are the pop singers Lindsay, Edele, Keavy and Sinead better known collectively?

742 *Proverbs*

'Procrastination is the thief of time.' What does procrastination mean?

743 *Military History*

What is the name of the battle in South Africa in 1879, between British and Zulu forces, at which a small British force won eleven VCs?

744 *Organizations*

In the field of conservation, the CPRE stands for what?

745 *Law*

What Latin phrase describes judicial matters not yet decided by a court of law or a judge, all discussion elsewhere therefore being prohibited?

746 *Theatre*

Table Manners, Living Together and *Round and Round the Garden*, a trilogy by Alan Ayckbourn, are known collectively under what title?

747 *The Suffragette Movement*

Who, with her daughter Christabel, founded the Women's Social and Political Union in 1903, taking the motto 'Deeds, not words'?

748 *Geography*

Which city in the Midlands stands on the River Derwent?

749 *Forms of Address*

A member of which rank in the hierarchy of the Catholic Church would be addressed as 'Your Eminence'?

750 *Written Language*

What are diacritic marks?

751 *Sports*

The men's athletics programme at the Olympics includes two walking events. Over what distances?

752 *English Law*

What name or title is held by the Treasury solicitor who represents the Crown in matrimonial cases?

753 *Popes*

Why is the Vatican in Rome called the Vatican?

754 *Motor Racing*

Who, in 1958, became the UK's first Formula One World Champion?

755 *Botany/Honours*

To be hederated means to be crowned with what?

756 *Earthquakes*

What is the difference between, for example, 6 on the Richter Scale and 7 on the Richter Scale?

757 *History*

What name is given to the open cart, used during the French Revolution to transport prisoners to the guillotine?

758 *Film*

In what connection are Peter Rogers and Gerry Thomas famous names in British cinema?

759 *Classic Television*

Which eponymous character, in a BBC series which ran for 26 years, had assistants called Leela, Romana, Peri, Melanie and Ace?

760 *The 1970s*

In which year in the 1970s were there three Popes?

761 *English Legal System*

What is the highest fine that magistrates may impose?

762 *European Literature*

Foucault's Pendulum, The Island of the Day Before and *The Name of the Rose* are works by which Italian novelist and scholar?

763 *Mythology and Legend*

Which mythological creature could only be tamed by a virgin maiden?

764 *Pop Art*

What is the name of the British painter and leading exponent of Pop whose most famous works include the cover design for the Beatles LP *Sergeant Pepper's Lonely Hearts Club Band*?

765 *Language*

What name connects a county in southern England and a four-wheeled carriage of the late nineteenth and early twentieth centuries?

766 *Shakespeare*

In which play, set on an enchanted tropical island, do the spirits Iris, Ceres, Juno and Arial appear?

767 *Arts and Crafts*

People can often be seen engaged in frottage in old churches. What would they be doing?

768 The Bible

Which book in the Old Testament is the first book of Moses?

769 English Law

If all 12 jurors are present, how many must agree to return a majority verdict?

770 Religion

Which rank in the Christian ministry takes its name from the Greek word meaning 'servant'?

771 History

In medieval England, murage was a tax levied for the upkeep of what?

772 The UK

In which English city is St Chad's Cathedral, the first Roman Catholic cathedral to be constructed in Britain since the Reformation?

773 Quotations

'No man is an island, entire of itself.' What is the name of the sixteenth-/seventeenth-century poet who wrote these lines?

774 Astronomy

As in the stars named Alpha Centauri or Alpha Canis Major, what is indicated by the designation 'alpha'?

775 Geography

The Drake Passage is a stretch of water separating which two landmasses?

776 Drama

What term or word describes the final unwinding of a complex storyline or the unravelling of the plot in drama?

777 Cricket

There are ten ways of dismissing a batsman including bowled out, run out, caught out, stumped, leg before wicket. Name one of the rarer five.

778 Music

'Lilliburlero' is the signature tune of which branch of the BBC?

779 The Royal Family

What relation is the present Queen to Queen Victoria?

780 Art and Famous Artists

What is the name of the Flemish artist who was appointed Principal Painter to their Majesties in 1632 at the court of Charles I?

781 Twentieth-century Music

The Threepenny Opera and *The Rise and Fall of the City of Mahogonny* were musical collaborations between the composer Kurt Weill and which celebrated German playwright?

782 The Bible/Wine

What name links a large wine bottle, equivalent to eight ordinary bottles, and a Biblical patriarch, said to have lived to 969 years old?

783 Classical Literature

'I sing of arms and the man' is a translation of the opening words of which ancient epic poem?

784 History

Which British monarch was the last to have been born outside the British Isles?

785 National Hunt Racing

What is the name of the race trainer who achieved the record of most National Hunt winners in the twentieth century?

786 Medicine

Epidemic parotiditis is the technical name for which common disease, characterized by swelling of the parotid, or salivary, glands?

787 Acronyms

By what acronym is radio detection and ranging, a device for determining the direction, range or presence of objects using radio waves, more commonly known?

788 Publishing

Which famous publishing house was founded in 1935 by Allen Lane to produce cheap paperback reprints of fiction?

789 History of Broadcasting

The first regular British television broadcasts started transmission in London in 1936. From where?

790 *Television*

Twenty years ago, he was one of Esther Rantzen's team of reporters on *That's Life!* Since then he has turned to writing, his best-known work being *Ballykissangel.* What is his name?

791 *The Royal Family*

Which member of the royal family is the president of the Commonwealth Games Federation?

792 *Geography*

Which body of water, the largest lake in the Alps, lies on the border of France and Switzerland?

793 *Science*

What name is given to the sheet of microfilm on which printed text is photographically reduced for filing?

794 *Geography*

In New Zealand, which major city was named after the Oxford college at which the city's founder had been educated?

795 *Medicine*

In relation to vision, what does the term 'accommodation' mean?

796 *Flags*

The fleur-de-lys is depicted on the flag of which Canadian province?

797 *Food and Drink*

Albacore, Bluefin, Yellowfin and Skipjack are members of which family of fish?

798 *Literary Expressions*

Writing devoted to recording and glorifying the lives of saints and martyrs is known as what?

799 *London Prisons*

The name of which Southwark prison, burned down in the Gordon Riots, has come to be used as a slang word for any such institution?

800 *Russian Literature*

How are three brothers called Dimitri, Ivan and Alyosha known collectively in the title of a novel by Dostoevsky?

801 *Annual Events*

The Nottingham Goose Fair, the Aldeburgh Benjamin Britten Festival and 'trick or treat' games are played countrywide. In which month?

802 *Medicine*

Cephalagia is a medical term for what very common complaint?

803 *Geography*

Which country on the Atlantic coast of South America is bounded to the north by Brazil and to the west by Argentina?

804 *The Bible*

The road between Jerusalem and Jericho is the setting for which of Jesus' parables?

805 *Human Anatomy*

The word 'volar' relates to which parts of the body?

806 *Politics*

The address of the headquarters of which organization is Millbank Tower, Millbank, London SW1P 4GT?

807 *Astronomy*

The term 'aphelion' in relation to the Earth or any planet in the universe describes what?

808 *History of Aviation*

Which de Havilland aircraft in 1949 was the world's first commercial jet airliner?

809 *Space Travel*

What specific name is given to the small auxiliary rockets that produce thrust, in the opposite direction to the direction of flight, and which are used to slow down a spacecraft?

810 *Monopoly*

There are four corner squares on a British Monopoly board. Name two of them.

811 *Food and Drink*

Made from the finely ground root of a tropical American plant, *Maranta arundinacea*, by what name is the starchy powder, usually used for thickening sauces, commonly known?

812 British History

What is the name of the hereditary disease thought to have caused the mental disturbance suffered by George III for long periods of his life?

813 Legend

According to legend, who cut the Gordian knot with his sword, thus laying claim to becoming ruler of Asia?

814 History of Films

Which actress, whose Hollywood career lasted only five years, starred in *High Noon, Rear Window* and *To Catch a Thief* in the 1950s?

815 Geography

Aconcagua, at nearly 7000 metres, is the highest mountain in the western hemisphere. In which mountain range does it lie?

816 Botany

Larkspur is also commonly known to gardeners by its Latin name. What is it?

817 Legal Affairs/Law and Order

In legal matters, which act of Parliament is abbreviated as PACE?

818 Chemistry

Which acid is also known as oil of vitriol?

819 Cartoon Characters

His creator originally wanted to give him the name Mortimer, but in the end deferred to his wife's choice. Which famous cartoon character was this?

820 Sport

What, in a sporting context in Japan, is a basho?

821 Eighteenth-century Literature

What is the full title of a book published in 1719 by Daniel Defoe: *The Life and Strange and Surprising Adventures of...* who?

822 The Solar System

Which planet is closest to the Sun?

823 *Film Lines*

'Nature, Mr Allnutt, is what we were put into this world to rise above': a classic line spoken by Katherine Hepburn to Humphrey Bogart. What was the film?

824 *Mythology*

How often did the Phoenix burn itself up, and then rise rejuvenated from the ashes?

825 *Roman Britain*

Which northern city was known to the Romans as Deva?

826 *English Law*

In which month do the Hilary sittings begin?

827 *Shakespeare and Astronomy*

Titania, Oberon and Puck are three of the 15 satellites of which planet?

828 *Annual Events*

The Edinburgh Military Tattoo, the Notting Hill Carnival and the Three Choirs Festival all take place during which month?

829 *Art*

The sculptures *Reclining Figure* and *Madonna and Child*, and the *Shelter Sketchbooks*, drawn during the Blitz while he was an official war artist, are well known works by which twentieth-century English sculptor?

830 *Television*

Who played Kavanagh QC on ITV?

831 *Music*

Which Yorkshire town is famous for its choral society, founded in 1836?

832 *Shakespeare*

Aegeon, a merchant of Syracuse, condemned to death in Ephesus, tells of how he and his wife were shipwrecked with their infant sons, identical twins and a pair of infant slaves, also identical twins. In which Shakespeare comedy?

833 *London*

Old Kent Road and Edgware Road both follow part of the path of which ancient Roman road?

834 *Children's Literature*

Winnie the Pooh loves honey. What is Paddington Bear's favourite food?

835 *Horse Racing*

Which annual flat race, run at Newmarket, took its name from the title of the heir to the Russian throne?

836 *Geography*

In which South American country are the Angel Falls, the highest waterfall in the world?

837 *Art and Famous Painters*

Which painter, best known for his portraits, was the first President of the Royal Academy?

838 *Science*

What word is used for an alloy of mercury with one or more other metals?

839 *Nursery Rhymes*

Who, after singing for his supper, was given 'white bread and butter'?

840 *Marching Tunes*

'Liberty Bell', 'The Stars and Stripes Forever' and 'The Washington Post' are military marches written by which American composer?

841 *Physics*

What name is given to the branch of physics based on the transmission of light through transparent filaments of glass or plastic?

842 *Geography*

In which sea are the groups of islands called the Greater Antilles and Lesser Antilles?

843 *Exploration*

For over 15 years, Marco Polo travelled through Asia, as a representative of which Mongol ruler?

844 *History of Engineering*

What is the name of the British engineer who built the Caledonian Canal, the Menai Suspension Bridge and St Katherine's Docks in London?

845 *Ships and the Sea*

Danforth, CQR and Stockless are three common forms of which piece of maritime equipment?

846 *Food and Drink*

What name is given, in South Africa, to strips of meat, dried and salted to preserve them?

847 *House of Commons Procedure*

The holder of which office is responsible for the security of the House?

848 *History of the Middle East*

The Arab–Israeli War of October 1973 began on an important Jewish holy day. Which one?

849 *London Streets*

Which street in London's Soho district is best known as the centre of the film industry?

850 *Shakespeare*

What name did Pericles, Prince of Tyre, give his daughter because she was born at sea?

851 *Geography*

What is the name of the arm of the Mediterranean Sea that lies between the north coast of Corsica and Italy?

852 *Birds*

What is the main distinguishing feature of all species of ratite, the most primitive group of living birds?

853 *Geography*

At around 4700 square miles, the Negev Desert occupies approximately 60 per cent of which Middle Eastern country?

854 *Nineteenth-century Literature*

How is Helen Graham, a young painter who has arrived in the neighbourhood with her son in mysterious circumstances, known in the title of a novel by Anne Brontë?

855 *Museums*

In which European city are the Treasuries of the Holy Roman Empire?

856 *Famous Lines*

'Men seldom make passes at girls who wear glasses.' Which American humorist wrote this line?

857 *Currencies*

What name is shared by the main units of currency in Cyprus, Egypt, Lebanon and Syria?

858 *Musicals*

The evil Judge Turpin, and Mrs Lovett who sells 'the worst pies in London' are characters in which Stephen Sondheim musical?

859 *Language*

Thanatology is the scientific study of what?

860 *The Bible*

What is the meaning of the word 'Gethsemane'?

861 *History of the USA*

George Armstrong Custer: what was his army rank at the time of his death at the Battle of the Little Big Horn?

862 *Famous Assassinations*

Who was assassinated by Gavrilo Princip on 28 June 1914?

863 *Shipping*

What alternative name is given to the loading line mark on the side of a ship's hull?

864 *Food and Drink*

What name is given to the Japanese speciality of batter-dipped, deep-fried pieces of fish or vegetables?

865 *Retailing*

Which US retailing giant is known by the acronym GUS?

866 *Terms of Speech*

Which term, for an informal, non-standard and allegedly classless English spoken by young people, takes its name from the accent's origins on the banks of the Thames in Essex and Kent?

867 *Republic of Ireland*

Which town – famous in song – is the county town of Kerry in Ireland?

868 *Science*

A 'refracting' telescope uses a converging lens to collect light. What does a 'reflecting' telescope use?

869 *English Law*

What term is used to describe those criminal offences which are tried only by magistrates without a jury?

870 *Music*

'In a Summer Garden', 'Walk to the Paradise Garden' and 'On Hearing the First Cuckoo in Spring': who is their English composer?

871 *Film/Music*

Which Russian composer wrote the film scores for the Eisenstein films *Alexander Nevsky* and *Ivan the Terrible*?

872 *Food and Drink*

A mixture of dried herbs, normally basil, fennel, marjoram, rosemary, sage and thyme, is named after which region of France?

873 *London*

In which famous building are there areas called Cloister Court, Star Chamber Court and Speaker's Court?

874 *Proverbs*

According to the proverb, 'many a mickle makes a…' what?

875 *Games*

In Belgium and France they are Doctor Olive, Professor Violet and Mademoiselle Rose. These are characters in which popular board game?

876 *Proverbs*

What, according to the saying, is the 'teacher of fools'?

877 *The Irish Peerage*

The holder of which title is the premier Duke and Marquess of Ireland?

878 *Professional Associations*

The BASW, with a membership of around 7500, represents which professional group?

879 Language/Words

What sort of word is a neologism?

880 Europe

Of which Italian region is Rome the capital?

881 Children's Literature

Which American children's novel tells the story of Cedric Errol, the young American heir to a British Earldom?

882 Music

What does the term 'ritardando' instruct a player to do?

883 Science

The eighteenth-/nineteenth-century Scottish physician and botanist, Daniel Rutherford, made the distinction, in 1772, between 'noxious air' and carbon dioxide. Which gas did he refer to as 'noxious air'?

884 Pop Music

The Unforgettable Fire, *The Joshua Tree* and *Achtung Baby* are all albums by which Irish pop group?

885 Counties

In which English county is there an area known since before the Domesday Book as Holland?

886 The British Monarchy

Of which royal house was Edward VII a member?

887 Music

In American musical terminology it is a 'sixteenth note'. What is it in English terminology?

888 English Heritage

What is the name of the English Heritage signs that both mark and describe the homes of the famous?

889 Twentieth-century Theatre

Mick, Aston and Davies, an old man, are the three characters in which Harold Pinter play?

890 British Political History

During the reign of which British monarch in the twentieth century were there no general elections?

891 *Plants*

What is the common name of the antirrhinum, which bears brightly coloured spiky flowers that gape like a mouth when a bee lands on the curved lip?

892 *Famous Women*

What was the name of the English theatrical manager who ran the Old Vic from 1912 and later the Sadlers Wells Theatre from 1931?

893 *Classical Music*

Vaughan Williams' song cycle 'On Wenlock Edge' is comprised of musical settings of whose poems?

894 *Science*

In aerodynamics, what word is used for the force that resists the forward motion or thrust of an object?

895 *American Presidents*

Which American President of the 1940s and 1950s had a famous sign on his desk that read: 'The buck stops here'?

896 *Card Games*

In the game of Blackjack, an Ace can be one of two values. What are they?

897 *Geography*

Off the southern coast of which continent are Magellan's Strait, Cockburn Channel and Beagle Channel?

898 *BBC Radio*

Which famous fictional village lies just off the B3980, six miles south of Borchester?

899 *The UK*

Founded in 1791, which is the UK's oldest national Sunday newspaper?

900 *Human Anatomy*

A crown, a neck and a root: which part or parts of the body are made up of these three sections?

901 *Words*

If something is described as being littoral, what would that tell you about its location?

902 *Twentieth-century Literature*

When his wife leaves to join a brothel, Adam Trask is left to bring up his two sons, Caleb and Aron. In which John Steinbeck novel?

903 *Religion*

In the Christian religion, what name is given to the highest of the Nine Orders of Angels?

904 *English Law*

In legal terms, what is a contemnor?

905 *Mythology*

Which mythical South American city had streets and palaces made of solid gold?

906 *Ships and the Sea*

What is a lee tide?

907 *The Old Testament*

Which book of the Old Testament was written by the prophet Jeremiah, mourning the destruction of the First Temple and of Jerusalem and the fate of the righteous King Josiah?

908 *Government*

Which government office has responsibility for British citizens abroad?

909 *Names*

Which girl's name is the English translation, not the English version, of the French name Marguerite?

910 *Slang*

What term is often used for obstinate petty officials, because they turn down reasonable requests on the grounds that their employment prospects may be jeopardized?

911 *Mythology*

Which dying mythological monster gave birth to Pegasus, the winged horse?

912 *Horse Racing*

On a race-card form-guide, if the letter F appears before its name the horse fell in that race. What specifically happened to the horse if the letter B appears before its name?

913 *The USA*

Of which state is Little Rock the capital city?

914 *Russian Literature*

In which novel is the eponymous heroine ruined because of her affair with Count Vronsky?

915 *Classic Films*

Montgomery Clift, Clark Gable and Eli Wallach are cowboys scratching a living in Reno. Marilyn Monroe is the recently divorced one-time stripper who meets up with them. What is the film?

916 *The British Armed Forces*

Which rank in the RAF is equivalent to a Sub-Lieutenant in the Royal Navy and a Lieutenant in the Army?

917 *Classical Music*

What nickname is given to Haydn's Symphony 92, which was performed when he came to Britain to receive an honorary doctorate?

918 *Literature*

What is the name of A.A. Milne's theatre adaptation of Kenneth Grahame's *The Wind in the Willows*?

919 *Television*

His name appears on our television screens several times a week. Who created *Coronation Street*?

920 *Poetry*

'The mirror crack'd from side to side'/"The curse is come upon me,"'cried who?

921 *Geography*

Spandau, Schöneberge and Charlottenburg are three districts of which European capital city?

922 *Musicals*

What is the name of the long-running musical, with book, lyrics and music by Willy Russell, that tells the tale of twins Eddie and Mickey separated as children who grow up in radically different situations?

923 *History*

Which British city was known as Lindum by the Romans?

924 *Asian Capital Cities*

Ulan Bator is the capital city of which Asian country?

925 *Ballet*

The famous ballerinas Alicia Markova and Lydia Sokolova are of which nationality?

926 *Weights and Measures*

How many square metres are there are there in a square kilometre?

927 *Judaism*

Containing the Mishnah, what name is specifically given to the collected teachings of the major Jewish scholars who flourished in the classic period of Rabbinical Judaism?

928 *Mythology*

What was the name of the Trojan prophetess who was cursed always to tell the truth but never to be believed?

929 *Zoology*

What is the name of the malodorous liquid sprayed by skunks when in danger?

930 *Cinema*

In which Oscar-winning 1998 film does the lead character initially write a play entitled *Romeo and Ethel, the Pirate's Daughter*?

931 *Literature*

Who was the Irish author of *The Quare Fellow* and *The Hostage*?

932 *Language and English Law*

In legal terms, and in relation to names, what is an agnomination?

933 *Language*

Which language, closely related to Hindi, is written in Arabic script and is the national language of Pakistan?

934 *Sport*

Which winter sport consists of the two disciplines cross-country skiing and rifle shooting?

935 Classic Television

Which actor, from 1963 to 1966, was the first television Doctor Who?

936 The Bible

From the Book of Proverbs, often misquoted: 'Pride goeth before...' What is the next word?

937 Olympics

The Val Barker Cup is awarded to the competitor adjudged to be the best stylist in which Olympic sport?

938 English Law

A department under the superintendence of the Attorney-General: what is the SFO?

939 Mythology

In Greek mythology, what was the effect of drinking water from the underworld river Lethe?

940 Twentieth-century Literature

Where did John Steinbeck get the title for his novel The Grapes of Wrath?

941 The British Monarchy

Maria Fitzherbert was the secret wife of which future nineteenth-century king?

942 Opera

Baba the Turk, Nick Shadow and Anne Trulove appear in which Stravinsky opera?

943 Phobias

Which meteorological phenomenon can give rise to astraphobia?

944 The Commonwealth

Hamilton is the capital of which British dependency?

945 Counties

The Quantock Hills, the Mendip Hills and the Blackdown Hills are all Areas of Outstanding Natural Beauty in which county?

946 Paris

What is the name of the modern exhibition centre in Paris housing the French National Gallery of Modern Art and the Centre for Industrial Design?

947 *The UK*

Brougham Castle, Furness Abbey and Lanercost Priory are all in which English county?

948 *House of Commons and the Media*

What term describes representatives of news media who have the authority of the Sergeant at Arms to enter the Members' Lobby when the house is sitting?

949 *The World of Islam*

What is a Muslim known as a 'Hafiz' able to do?

950 *Annual Events*

Which annual event takes place in the City of London on the second Saturday in November?

951 *French Geography*

Avignon, Arles and Lyon are all on which major river?

952 *World War One*

The scene of fierce fighting in World War One, in which country is the Gallipoli Peninsular?

953 *Transport*

In terms of international scheduled services, which airline is the world's largest?

954 *Television*

For which television character on Channel 4 is the American actress Calista Flockhart best known?

955 *Titles*

Which title, used until Tudor times for persons appointed to act as regents for underaged sovereigns, was assumed by Oliver Cromwell and his son during the Commonwealth?

956 *Counties*

Salcombe, Budleigh Salterton and Dawlish are on the coast of which English county?

957 *The UK*

Stilton cheese is protected by its own trademark that prescribes the method of production and limits its manufacture to just three counties of England. Name one of them.

958 *Nursery Rhymes*

Who, in a nursery rhyme, cultivated argent carillons and pilgrims badges in her garden?

959 *Medicine*

Creutzfeldt-Jakob Disease or CJD is a degenerative condition affecting which organ of the body?

960 *The Christian Year*

In the Christian calendar, what name is given to the days in spring on which special prayers are said for the newly sown crops to produce a good harvest?

961 *Telecommunications*

If you dial 153 on a telephone, which service do you reach?

962 *Africa*

The largest lake in Africa is also the chief reservoir for the River Nile. What is its name?

963 *Television*

What type of programming does the satellite channel Paramount exclusively screen?

964 *Artistic Organizations*

Its membership is limited to 80 and members must be either painters, engravers, sculptors or architects. What is the name of this prestigious society?

965 *Newspapers*

The Mirror Group owns two national Sunday newspapers: The *Sunday Mirror* and which other?

966 *Medicine*

Tachycardia means a quick heartbeat. What is tachypnoea?

967 *Films*

The 1999 release *Rogue Trader* tells the story of the man who brought about the collapse of the merchant bank Barings in 1995. What is his name?

968 *Television*

By what abbreviation is Channel 4 Wales commonly known?

969 *Spanish Literature*

Which fictional character tilted at windmills thinking them to be giants?

970 *Music*

What name is given to a chord of which the notes are performed, not simultaneously, but in rapid succession, either ascending or descending?

971 *Business*

What is the name of the official weekly paper that lists, among other matters, bankruptcies, ending of partnerships, winding-up orders and changes in company names?

972 *Quotations*

'I am just going outside and may be some time.' Whose famous last words?

973 *History of Films*

Which 1945 classic film is the story of the love affair between Dr Alec Harvey and Laura Jesson?

974 *The UK*

The Rollright Stones, the White Horse of Uffington and Dorchester Abbey are all in which English county?

975 *Bridge*

What name is given to the player who reveals his hand, and sits out the game?

976 *Language*

What term describes the group of European languages including French, Spanish and Italian that are descended from Latin?

977 *Pop Music*

The Quarrymen, Johnny and the Moondogs and The Beat Boys were all earlier names used by which 1960s British pop group?

978 *History of Russia*

How is Sophie, the German wife of Peter III of Russia, more commonly known?

979 *Television*

Two sisters from north London. Tracey lives in a nice house in Chigwell, Sharon lives in a council tower block in Edmonton but she moves in with Tracey when both their husbands are jailed for 12 years for armed robbery. Which BBC sitcom is this?

980 *Medicine*

What name is given to any artificial device that does duty for a bodily organ or member, a glass eye or false limb, for example?

981 *History*

Everyone old enough to remember the period seems able to remember what they were doing on the date that President John F. Kennedy died. What was the date?

982 *Proverbs*

'Whom the Gods would destroy, they first…' what?

983 *Ships and the Sea*

In which of Nelson's major victories was his flagship called HMS *Vanguard*?

984 *Alternative Medicine*

What term is used to describe the form of medicine that seeks to treat the whole person, rather than just the parts of the body in which a disease or illness may be found?

985 *British Animals*

Dartmoor, Dale and Welsh Mountain are all native breeds of which animal?

986 *Wine*

What name is given to the wine made from grapes picked when frozen on the vine?

987 *Transport*

You can catch a passenger ferry from Kingston-upon-Hull to one of two Dutch ports. Name either of them.

988 *Opera*

Falstaff by Verdi is principally based on which play by Shakespeare?

989 *World Politics*

By what Hebrew name, which literally means 'gathering', is the Israeli parliament known?

990 *Museums*

The Ashmolean Museum was the first purpose-built public museum in England. It opened in 1683. In which city?

991 *Literature*

What is the name of the hero who is kidnapped in Robert Louis Stevenson's *Kidnapped*?

992 *Technology*

Increasingly used in public spaces, and still the subject of debate, what is CCTV?

993 *Annual Events*

Crufts Dog Show and the Cheltenham National Hunt Festival both take place in which month?

994 *Literature and the Cub Scouts*

What name, the leader of the wolf pack in Kipling's *Jungle Books*, is now used to designate the leader of a pack of Cub Scouts?

995 *Classic Radio*

J. Peasemould Gruntfuttock, Rambling Syd Rumpo and the limp-wristed Sandy were all characters played by Kenneth Williams on which classic radio comedy series of the 1960s?

996 *Banking/Commerce*

What do the initials MLR stand for?

997 *Christianity*

What name is given to the occasion when the Angel Gabriel informed the Virgin Mary that she would bear a son, Jesus?

998 *Scotland*

At which village do members of the MacDonald clan gather on 13 February each year, in memory of a brutal slaughter perpetrated on the clan by the Campbells in 1692?

999 *Field Sports*

Which well-known Leicestershire hunt is named after a village near Loughborough?

1000 *Physics*

What is defined as the rate of flow of charge through a circuit and is measured in amperes?

1001 *Geography*

Which country is known by the abbreviation UAE?

1002 *Common Abbreviations*

The written abbreviation i.e. is a shortening of which Latin phrase?

1003 *The USA*

The Teamsters Union is a major trade union in the United States. What is a teamster?

1004 *UK History*

What name was given to the group of craftsmen who, fearing unemployment, destroyed textile machines between 1811 and 1816?

1005 *Mythology*

Commander of the Greek army in the Trojan War, he was killed by his wife Clytemnestra and her lover on his return. What was his name?

1006 *European Landmarks*

What is the name of the city in northern France, famed for its Gothic cathedral, where French kings were traditionally crowned?

1007 *Shakespeare*

The entire action of Romeo and Juliet takes place in one month of the year. Which month?

1008 *History of Russia*

Which Soviet leader adopted a name which meant 'man of steel'?

1009 *Trade Unions*

By what shortened name is the British actors' trade union known?

1010 *Literature*

Which crime writer also wrote romantic novels, under the pseudonym Mary Westmacott?

1011 *Art*

The sixteenth-/seventeenth-century artist Nicholas Hilliard is chiefly associated with his paintings of which English monarch?

1012 *Crime in the USA*

Which famous epithet was coined for the 1930s gangster John Dillinger?

1013 *Folklore*

In the annals of folklore, in which group of British islands are the remnants of the submerged land of Lyonesse?

1014 *Charles Dickens*

Nell Trent lives in a shop with her grandfather, who owns it. When he gambles away all their money they are forced to take to the road as beggars: in which Dickens novel?

1015 *The UK*

Milton's Cottage, the Hellfire Caves and Chequers are all in which English county?

1016 *New Zealand*

What type of natural feature are the Tasman, the Franz Josef and the Fox?

1017 *Food and Drink*

Grenadine is cordial syrup made from which fruit?

1018 *Literature*

Of which Jane Austen novel is Anne Elliot the heroine?

1019 *World Heritage Sites*

The UK has 17 sites on the World Heritage list. Only one of them is in Northern Ireland. What is it?

1020 *The UK*

The major part of the Forest of Bowland lies in which English county?

1021 *World War One*

What name, derived from a supposed outburst by Kaiser Wilhelm, was adopted by British soldiers who survived the retreat from Mons and other early battles of World War One?

1022 *The British Monarchy*

Whom did the son of Ernest, Duke of Saxe-Coburg, marry on 10 February 1840?

1023 *Science*

Benthos is a name given to the plant and animal life found where?

1024 *Proverbs*

'Nothing succeeds like…' what?

1025 *Religion*

Which branch of Christianity traces its origins to John Smyth in the seventeenth century?

1026 *British Associations*

TOWA is the controlling body in the UK of which outdoor sport, which was an Olympic event from 1900 until 1920?

1027 *Military*

What name is given to the type of shelter made of a corrugated steel sheet, named after the British mining engineer who invented it?

1028 *The UK*

Established in 1919, which government department is responsible for around 2.6 million acres of land and gets some of its government funds from the sale of timber?

1029 *Mythology*

Which profession uses a representation of the wand carried by Hermes, the messenger of the Gods, as its insignia?

1030 *Music*

What is the title of the National Anthem of the Republic of Ireland?

1031 *The Professions*

Members of which profession are sometimes referred to as the 'Fourth Estate'?

1032 *Food and Drink*

The lobby group CAMRA: for what is CAMRA an abbreviation?

1033 *Proverbs*

'Penny wise and…' what?

1034 *Twentieth-century Literature*

What is the name of the American novelist and short story writer who achieved major fictional success with the publication of *Lake Wobegon Days* in 1985?

1035 *Words*

From the Greek for 'image breaker', what word describes a person who attacks cherished beliefs?

1036 *Parliament*

What name is given to public bills that are introduced by backbenchers in the House of Commons?

1037 *Greek Mythology*

King Minos was a legendary king of which Mediterranean island?

1038 *Chemistry*

Which metallic element is added to steel to make it stainless?

1039 *Geography*

New Zealand, Samoa, the Cook Islands and Hawaii are part of which group of Pacific islands?

1040 *Geography*

Orology is the scientific study of which geographical features?

1041 *Golf*

In the Open Championship, after how many holes does the 'Cut' take place?

1042 *The Bible*

In which modern-day country is the biblical Mount Sinai?

1043 *Cards*

Which set of illustrated cards is divided into two groups called the major and minor Arcana?

1044 *Films and Quotes*

Who, playing Julius Caesar in *Carry on Cleo*, famously cried, 'Infamy! Infamy! They've all got it in for me!'?

1045 *British Politics*

Which ancient crown land and estates has a chancellor who has a seat in the British cabinet?

1046 *Popular Music*

From 'September Song' by Maxwell Anderson, 'It's a long, long while from…' name the next three words.

1047 *Shakespeare*

'Good night, sweet Prince, And flights of angels sing thee to thy rest!' Which Prince?

1048 *Higher Education*

Part of London University, Wye College near Ashford in Kent, specializes in which field?

1049 Sport

Which word for a sports hall comes from the Greek for 'school for naked exercise'?

1050 Classic Television

Originally played on television in the 1960s by Dennis Price and Ian Carmichael, which upper-class toff and his valet were portrayed by Hugh Laurie and Stephen Fry in the early 1990s?

1051 Inventions

Two French brothers, in the eighteenth century, pioneered hot-air balloon flight. What was their surname?

1052 Boxing

The Manassa Mauler was the nickname of which legendary American heavyweight champion?

1053 The World of Islam

What honorific title, derived from the Arabic for 'miraculous sign of God' is bestowed upon distinguished members of the Shi'ite religious hierarchy?

1054 Pop Music

The Mancunian Mick Hucknall is the singer in which successful pop group?

1055 The Kennedy Clan

What is the name of the famous Kennedy compound on Cape Cod that is their summer retreat?

1056 The Natural World

Found in Asia, the gavial or gharial is a close relative of which reptile?

1057 The USA/Entertainment

The five Ringling brothers – Albert, Otto, Alfred, Charles and John – founded America's most famous what?

1058 Television

What is the title of the BBC comedy, written by and starring Victoria Wood, that goes behind the scenes in a works canteen?

1059 Music

How many notes are there in a Pentatonic scale?

1060 *History of Pop*

'My Generation', 'Substitute' and 'Pictures of Lily' were all hits for which English pop group, once famous for smashing their instruments at the end of their live performances?

1061 *Films of the 1990s*

For which 1995 Disney animated feature film did Tom Hanks provide the voice for Woody and Tim Allen provide the voice for Buzz Lightyear?

1062 *Twentieth-century Figures*

In which country were Emiliano Zapata and Pancho Villa revolutionary fighters in the early part of the twentieth century?

1063 *Anatomy*

What is phrenology the study of?

1064 *Mathematics*

In a right-angled triangle, the square of the hypotenuse is equal to the sum of the squares on the other two sides. How is this tenet popularly known?

1065 *Music of the 1960s*

The brothers Brian, Carl and Dennis Wilson, with their cousin Mike Love and Al Jardine, were the original line-up of which legendary pop group – exponents of the surf sound?

1066 *The European Union*

There are twenty EU commissioners. Every member state sends one, but five countries send two: Germany, France and the UK are three of these countries, which are the other two?

1067 *Science*

What is a Bourdon gauge used to measure?

1068 *Opera*

In which Wagner opera does the hero marry Elsa, on condition that she does not ask his name nor where he comes from?

1069 *The British Monarchy*

Who was the last reigning British monarch to die and not be succeeded by a son or daughter?

1070 *The UK*

Which town in Shropshire is named after St Oswald, who was killed there in 642?

1071 *Hobbies and Collections*

What is listed in a standard SEABY catalogue published by Spink, an authority in the field?

1072 *Famous Courts of Law*

It's commonly known as the Old Bailey. What is its official name?

1073 *English Law*

The Bar Council is the controlling body for barristers in England and Wales. What name is given to the body that controls solicitors?

1074 *Betting and Gaming*

What is the popular name for the Horse Race Totalizer Board?

1075 *Finance*

What is the colour of the American Express Centurion credit card, which gives holders unlimited spending?

1076 *Scottish Law*

There are three possible verdicts in Scottish law: guilty, not guilty and what?

1077 *The Royal Family*

The Castle of Mey, at Caithness, is one of the three residences of which member of the royal family?

1078 *Politics*

What is the name of the seat on which the Lord Chancellor, in his capacity as Speaker, sits in the House of Lords?

1079 *The Business World*

Traditionally the Lutine Bell in Lloyds in the City of London is rung once… to announce what?

1080 *Cricket*

Including players and umpires, what's the maximum number of people who can be on a cricket pitch at the same time?

1081 *History*

What does the Rufus Stone in the New Forest mark?

1082 *Britain*

There were seven Saxon kingdoms in ancient Britain in the sixth and seventh centuries. Northumbria, Mercia and Wessex were three of them. Name two of the other four.

1083 *Poetry in the 1960s*

The poets Roger McGough, Brian Patten and Adrian Henri are all identified with which English city?

1084 *Domestic Animals*

Charollais, Simmental and Dexter are breeds of which domestic animal?

1085 *London Names*

Which area of north London takes its name from an inn built there in the early nineteenth century in the style of an Alpine chalet?

1086 *The British Empire*

Which term, derived from the Sanskrit word for 'king', is used to describe British sovereignty in India?

1087 *Commonwealth*

What is the capital of the Falkland Islands?

1088 *The North of England*

Which town in West Yorkshire has a name derived from the Latin for 'broken bridge'?

1089 *Business Abbreviations*

In France it is SA; in Germany it is AG and in the Netherlands it is NV. What is it in the UK?

1090 *Poetry*

What is the title of the poem by William Wordsworth that begins: 'Earth has not anything to show more fair'?

1091 *Words*

How is senescence in human beings more commonly known?

1092 *Films of the 1990s*

In which 1993 film did Robin Williams play two roles: one being Daniel Hillard and other being the character in the title of the film?

1093 *The UK*

The first of this type of religious building in the UK was established in Woking in Surrey in 1890. What is it?

1094 *The British Monartchy*

Which monarch made Buckingham Palace the official London residence of the sovereign?

1095 *France*

Britain is symbolized by the female figure Britannia. What is the name of the young woman who symbolizes France?

1096 *The UK*

What is the name of the longest canal in the UK, some 240 miles long, that connects London and Birmingham?

1097 *Films of the 1990s*

What is the name of the 1997 film starring Julia Roberts as a go-getting New York food critic who is horrified when her pal, Michael, announces his forthcoming marriage?

1098 *Mythology*

Who, according to Greek mythology, was the first mortal woman?

1099 *History*

During which British monarch's reign were the American colonies lost?

1100 *British Organizations*

The LDOS is a society founded in 1831 to preserve Sunday as a national day of rest. What does LDOS stand for?

1101 *Landmarks*

What sort of building is colloquially know as the Boston Stump, a well-known landmark in Boston, Lincolnshire?

1102 *Dates*

Which Middle Eastern state came into being on 14 May 1948?

1103 *Musicals*

The satirical musical *Oh! What a Lovely War* tells the story in songs and music-hall routines of which twentieth-century conflict?

1104 *Golf*

In the game of golf, one shot under par is a birdie. What is two shots under par called?

1105 *Business and Commerce*

Why is the American Ray Kroc a famous name in the fast-food business?

1106 *British History*

Who, in December 1170, was murdered by Reginald Fitzurse, William de Tracy, Hugh de Morvile and Richard le Breton?

1107 *The UK*

What botanical symbol is used by the Countryside Agency to mark National Trails?

1108 *The USA*

What is the significance in American politics of the donkey and the elephant?

1109 *The Highway Code*

When traffic lights at a road junction are red, what comes next?

1110 *Chemistry*

What name is given to the substance in which the 'solute' is dissolved to make a solution?

1111 *English Law*

Young people aged between sixteen and eighteen can lawfully buy two types of alcoholic drink with a meal in a restaurant. Name either of the two.

1112 *Sport*

Which sport or activity was invented by Major Ernst Killander in 1918 in Sweden and requires the use of a map and compass?

1113 *Science*

Two elements are liquid at room temperature (i.e. 68–70°F). Bromine is one. What is the other?

1114 *Literature*

With reference to Francis Bacon, who lived in the sixteenth and seventeenth centuries, what is the Baconian Theory or the Baconian Heresy?

1115 Geography

Between which two points on a map or globe does a meridian run?

1116 Medicine

In the context of hospitals, what is an ICU?

1117 Military

What is the motto of the SAS (Special Air Service)?

1118 The Royal Navy

At Portsmouth, HMS *Victory* is in dry dock and so never goes anywhere. Why does HMS *Nelson*, also at Portsmouth, never go anywhere?

1119 Literature/Poetry

The poetic work *Summoned by Bells* is an autobiographical account of the early years of which Poet Laureate?

1120 Driving Regulations

A moped is defined by the DVLA as being a motorbike that cannot go faster than what speed?

1121 Medicine

Gastralgia is pain where in the body?

1122 Wimbledon Tennis

How many players in total, men and women, are seeded in the singles championship?

1123 The Bible

In Genesis, five cities of the plain are mentioned. Which two were destroyed by fire and brimstone because of their wickedness?

1124 Nobel Prizes

The founder of the Lambaréné Hospital in Africa was awarded the Nobel Peace Prize in 1952. What was his name?

1125 Culinary Terms

What name links the capital of Ukraine with a piece of chicken filled with butter and fried in breadcrumbs?

1126 Geography

The ruined Castle Urquhart overlooks which Scottish loch?

1127 *Transport*

What, in Italy, is the Pendolino?

1128 *Sport*

Which London football club, founded in 1886, is named after its original proximity to a government arms factory?

1129 *World Religions*

The Four Noble Truths and The Eightfold Path are two important teachings of what religion?

1130 *History*

Subject of a famous Picasso painting, the bombing of Guernica took place during which twentieth-century conflict?

1131 *Poetry*

The opening lines of which seventeenth-century epic poem proclaim that its subject is 'man's first disobedience'?

1132 *Computing*

What term, usually associated with a restaurant, is used for the list of options or programs available to the user?

1133 *Landmarks*

Apart from being rocks, what links the following: Bell Rock, Bishop Rock and Wolf Rock?

1134 *Sherlock Holmes*

Sherlock Holmes went to the fictional university of 'Camford' to investigate Professor Presbury. What is the more usual combination of the two ancient university names?

1135 *Sport*

The governing body in the UK of which sport is based at the Queen's Club in West London?

1136 *Films of the 1990s*

In which 1998 film does Bruce Willis play an oil driller recruited by NASA to plant a nuclear bomb in an asteroid on a collision course with Earth?

1137 *Films of the 1990s*

In two films, released in 1991 and 1993, Angelica Huston played Morticia and Raul Julia played Gomez. What was their family name?

1138 *Polar Exploration*

What was the name of the Norwegian who beat Captain Scott to the South Pole in 1911?

1139 *English History*

Who was Lord Protector in England from 1658 to 1659?

1140 *Chemistry*

Called brimstone in medieval times, which yellow element is used in the production of the acid H_2So_4?

1141 *The Royal Family*

What is the relationship between the Duke of Kent and Princess Alexandra?

1142 *Food and Drink*

Which rice, grown in the foothills of the Himalayas, literally translates as 'fragrant'?

1143 *English Poetry*

The opening lines from a famous ode by Shelley: 'Hail to thee blithe spirit! Bird thou never wert.' Which bird is the ode addressed to?

1144 *Musical Instruments*

The bouzouki is a stringed instrument from which country?

1145 *North Africa*

Which country on the Mediterranean Sea lies between Algeria and Libya?

1146 *Sport*

The Chicago Bulls, The LA Lakers and the Detroit Pistons are all American teams that play which sport?

1147 *Shakespeare*

Who, in a Shakespeare play, after the death of her lover brings about her own death with the bite of an asp?

1148 *The Internet*

What term is used to mean adding a Web site address to an online address book, so that the site may be easily visited again?

1149 *Medicine*

Renal calculus is the medical term for what, quite common, condition?

1150 *History/Religion*

In the twelfth century, Nicholas Breakspear became the first and only Englishman to hold which office?

1151 *Netball*

In netball, two players can only move within one third of the court. Name the position of either player.

1152 *Geography*

Which Crown colony, at the western end of the Mediterranean Sea, was ceded to the UK by the Treaty of Utrecht in 1713?

1153 *Pop Music*

The albums *Ocean Drive* and *Postcards from Heaven* were bestselling albums for which band?

1154 *Shakespeare and Modern Italy*

In which Italian city is there a medieval trough which, it is claimed, is the tomb of Juliet Capulet?

1155 *The Nineteenth Century*

The Battle of Gettysburg in July 1863 was a turning point in which conflict?

1156 *Sport*

Eddy Merckx and Miguel Indurain are both five-times winners of which marathon sporting event?

1157 *World War Two*

As opposed to doing military service, where did the Bevin Boys work?

1158 *Geography*

Which country is the second largest in South America after Brazil, and, with an Atlantic coastline, shares land borders with Chile, Bolivia, Paraguay, Brazil and Uruguay?

1159 *Explorers*

Which early seventeenth-century English explorer had three North American waterways named after him: a river, a bay and a strait?

1160 *Cashpoints*

In order to use a cashpoint, you require a card with a PIN. What does PIN stand for in this context?

1161 *Physics*

What term is used to refer to the study of flight paths of projectiles, especially those from firearms?

1162 *Table Tennis*

After how many points do the players change service?

1163 *The Animal Kingdom*

Living in Indonesia, and growing up to 3 metres in length, the Komodo dragon is the largest type of which reptile?

1164 *Geology*

The Earth is usually described as consisting of three layers. The crust is one, name one of the other two.

1165 *Television/Literature*

Who is the creator of Inspector Morse?

1166 *Languages*

Greek is one of the two official languages of Cyprus. What is the other?

1167 *Anatomy*

What in the human body are the quadriceps, the gluteus maximus and the pectoralis major?

1168 *Law*

What term is used to refer to a charge of treason brought against a head of state?

1169 *History*

King Idris, the last monarch of Libya, was deposed in 1969 by whom?

1170 *Geometry*

What term is used in geometry to apply to plane or solid figures that have the same shape and size?

1171 *Literature*

Notre Dame de Paris by the French novelist Victor Hugo is better known to us by its English title. What is it?

1172 *Animals*

What is the name of the large, shaggy ox commonly found on the Tibetan plateau?

1173 *Media*

What service, in the Republic of Ireland, is abbreviated as RTE?

1174 *Geography*

In what ocean do the Seychelles lie?

1175 *Biology*

Many living things need oxygen, but which chemical element is essential to all living things?

1176 *Literature*

In *The Canterbury Tales*, what in Canterbury Cathedral are the pilgrims going to visit?

1177 *Greek Mythology*

Who beheaded Medusa and later rescued Andromeda?

1178 *Famous Couples*

The Somali-born model Iman has a famous husband. What is his name?

1179 *Road Systems*

We use M for motorway. For federal highways in the USA, Americans use the letter I, meaning what?

1180 *Geography*

Which mountain range extends down the whole length of the Italian peninsula?

1181 *Science*

What term is used to describe iron or steel that has been coated with zinc in order to protect it from corrosion?

1182 *Language*

MI5 and MI6. What does MI stand for?

1183 *Food and Drink*

Meaning literally 'table of buttered bread', what word is used for the Swedish assortment of hot and cold dishes served as a buffet?

1184 *Cricket*

Stumps to stumps, how long is a cricket pitch?

1185 English Cities

According to tradition, Lady Godiva rode naked through the streets of which city to persuade her husband to reduce taxes?

1186 Countries

At 3776 metres, the extinct volcano Fujiyama is the highest and most sacred mountain in which Far Eastern country?

1187 Motor Car Manufacturers

Which motor car manufacturer makes the Frontera, the Tigra and the Vectra?

1188 Natural History

Barnacle, Greylag, Brent and Canada are types of which bird?

1189 The Americas

Which country has land borders with the United States, Belize and Guatemala?

1190 Famous Catchphrases

Whose famous sporting strategy was 'float like a butterfly, sting like a bee'?

1191 Figures of Speech

Which figure of speech is used when someone is said to be that which he or she only resembles? For example, 'He is a tiger'?

1192 Geography

What name is given to a lake formed by a loop in a river that becomes separated from the main flow of the river?

1193 Aviation History

The World War One German flying ace, Manfred von Richthofen, was known by what colourful nickname?

1194 The Arts

In which field of the arts is Cameron Mackintosh a famous name?

1195 Scotland

With an area of 27.5 square miles, which is the largest loch in Scotland?

1196 Religion

What is the meaning of the word 'polytheism'?

1197 *English Law*

Which high legal post is abbreviated as DPP?

1198 *Television*

The BBC against-the-clock programme *Ground Force*: what activity does it cover?

1199 *Geography*

Which group of Pacific islands are also called the Friendly Islands?

1200 *Television*

The registration mark of whose pink Rolls Royce in *Thunderbirds* is FAB1?

1201 *Australia*

What, designed by the English engineer Sir Ralph Freeman in the 1920s, stretches from Dawes Point to Milsons Point in Sydney?

1202 *Media*

Who is the most famous name connected with the independent television company, Ardent Productions?

1203 *Music*

In which of his famous operas did Rossini include an alpenhorn?

1204 *Theatre*

What is the name of Eliza Doolittle's phonetics expert in George Bernard Shaw's *Pygmalion*?

1205 *Sport*

What is the name of the sports meeting for disabled athletes, held every four years in conjunction with the Olympic Games?

1206 *English Law*

What term is commonly used in English law to refer to a minor under the protection of the High Court?

1207 *Sport*

Edward Heath is the only British prime minister to have captained a British team to victory in an international sporting event whilst still in office. Which sport?

1208 *Geography*

Which large inland body of water in the USA is more saline than any of the world's oceans?

1209 *Agriculture*

What word describes food produced without the use of chemical fertilizers or pesticides?

1210 *Catchphrases*

The catch phrase 'do I not like that' will forever be associated with which former England football manager?

1211 *Politics*

In the UK it is the House of Lords. What name is given to the upper house of the parliaments of France, Ireland, Spain, Belgium and Italy?

1212 *English Poetry*

What name is given to a lyric poem of 14 lines in iambic pentameter?

1213 *Geography*

Which island is separated from India by the Palk Strait?

1214 *Science*

Heat energy may be transferred by three methods. Name two of the three.

1215 *Abbreviations*

Which agency of the United Nations is known by the initials WHO?

1216 *Ships*

What cargo does a ship known as a ULCC carry?

1217 *Charitable Organizations*

In the UK, the PDSA promotes correct care of domestic pets. What does PDSA stand for?

1218 *Sport*

In which city is county cricket played at Sophia Gardens and Nationwide League football at Ninian Park?

1219 *Music*

From the Latin for goat, what term is used to describe a piece of music expressing the light-hearted and the whimsical?

1220 *The English Monarchy*

Elizabeth I died in 1603. Which queen was on the English throne a hundred years later?

1221 *Politics*

John Major entered the House of Commons in the year that Mrs Thatcher entered Downing Street. Which year was this?

1222 *English Law*

In legal terms, what is commutation?

1223 *History*

The Defenestration of Prague in May 1618 was one of the events of the Thirty Years War. What is defenestration?

1224 *Geography*

The islands of Bali, Sumatra and Java are all part of which Asian country?

1225 *Language*

What name, still in use for seats of learning, was given to the school founded in Athens by Plato?

1226 *Medicine*

What is the medical term for tooth decay?

1227 *Food and Drink*

What French word describes wine at room temperature?

1228 *Trade Unions*

The AUT represents workers in which field?

1229 *Politics*

Who was the leader of the Opposition from 1975 to 1979?

1230 *History of the American West*

How are two outlaws Robert Parker and Harry Longbaum better known in the history of the West?

1231 *Victorian Literature*

In which H. Rider Haggard novel does a big game hunter and guide lead a group into the African interior in search of George Curtis, and discover the remains of an ancient civilization and great riches?

1232 *History*

Which saint was martyred at Verulamium in the third or fourth century AD and was the first British martyr?

1233 *The Arts*

In Germany, what sort of an event is a Sangerfest?

1234 *Mathematics*

How many minutes are there in one degree?

1235 *Language*

From the French meaning 'cold blood', what term is used for coolness or indifference?

1236 *Geography*

Which Welsh county does not have a border with any other county?

1237 *Names*

What female Christian name is derived from the Latin word meaning 'foreseeing'?

1238 *Government*

OFSTED is the office for what?

1239 *Geography*

Which Alpine pass in Switzerland is a road built by Napoleon in 1800 to 1805?

1240 *Politics*

Who is the official representative of the House of Commons to the sovereign?

1241 *Phrases*

How does Descartes' famous phrase 'Cogito, ergo sum' translate into English?

1242 *The Arts*

In which field is the Japanese-born woman Mitsuko Uchida a famous name?

1243 *Airlines*

In which state of the USA are Aloha Airlines based?

1244 *Films of the 1930s*

A machine worker played by Charlie Chaplin suffers temporary derangement as he tightens the bolts on a factory treadmill to a clock-like tempo: a famous scene from which film?

1245 *Science*

On which logarithmic scale, which runs from 0 to 14, does 7 indicate neutral, below 7 acid and above 7 alkali?

1246 *Classical Music*

In which section of the orchestra might you find an anvil, a triangle, a rattle and a gong?

1247 *Educational Qualifications*

If someone has qualified with an HND, what qualification have they obtained?

1248 *The Bible*

The American Negro song 'Dem Bones' was inspired by the story of which Old Testament prophet?

1249 *Geography*

What name is given to Europe and Asia, when described as a single land mass or entity?

1250 *Human Anatomy*

Which nerve runs from the retina and carries messages to the brain?

1251 *Hobbies*

What is a gricer also known as?

1252 *Sport*

The Warwickshire Cup and the Waterloo Cup are competed for in which sport?

1253 *The USA*

The neighbouring cities of Minneapolis and St Paul – known as the Twin Cities – are the two largest cities in which state?

1254 *Airports*

If your luggage tag reads BHX, to which British city would you be flying?

1255 *Art*

A set of three tablets, for example three painted panels, hinged together to make one piece is known as what?

1256 *Art*

The death of which Shakespearean character was painted by the Pre-Raphaelite Sir John Millais in 1852?

1257 *Weights and Measures*

Which imperial measurement is defined by statute as 640 acres?

1258 *Foreign Words*

What would you get if someone sent you a billet-doux?

1259 *Famous Quotations*

What, according to Oscar Wilde, is the 'curse of the drinking classes'?

1260 *History*

In which half of which century did the Hanoverian dynasty begin in Britain and the Act of Union unite England and Scotland?

1261 *Environment*

Which now world-wide environmental group was formed in the USA by David Brower in 1969?

1262 *The UK*

On which English moor is the famous Jamaica Inn, long associated with smugglers, made famous in a story by Daphne du Maurier?

1263 *Television*

In *ER*, the American hospital series, what does the ER stand for?

1264 *The British Monarchy*

Who was the mother of the third of Henry VIII's children to accede to the throne?

1265 *Politics*

The holders of the same office in the 1950s and 1960s became respectively the Earl of Avon and the Earl of Stockton. Who were they?

1266 *Classical Music*

The song cycle 'Our Hunting Fathers' by Benjamin Britten is set to a text by which poet?

1267 *Famous Couples*

Who is the famous husband of the actress Jean Boht?

1268 *Women in Sport*

Charlotte Brew, Jenny Pitman and Geraldine Rees have all achieved 'firsts' associated with which famous sporting event?

1269 Medicine

For what sort of test would a standard Snellen chart be used?

1270 The Arts

William Henry Fox Talbot was a nineteenth-century pioneer in which field?

1271 Slogans

Used since 1986, what is the advertising slogan for the German car manufacturer Audi?

1272 Religion

By what physical means do pilgrims to Lourdes hope to be cured?

1273 Television

What name, as producer and/or writer, over the years, connects the series *Are You Being Served?*, *'Allo, 'Allo*, *Dad's Army* and *Hi-Di-Hi*?

1274 Television in the 1980s

The situation comedy *A Fine Romance* starred which real-life married couple?

1275 Science

What is the most abundant element in the universe?

1276 World War One

In what way did Billy Bishop of Canada, Rene Fonck of France, Edward Mannock of Britain and Eddie Rickenbacker of the USA make their names in World War One?

1277 The Royal Family

At the State Opening of Parliament, what is Queen Alexandra's State Coach usually used for?

1278 Language

From which modern language do the words embargo, flotilla and bonanza derive?

1279 Religion

The Hadith is a collection of the sayings and actions of which prophet?

1280 Wars and Battles

Fort Sumter in 1861 saw the first hostilities of which war?

1281 *The New Testament*

What name connects the woman disciple who washed the feet of Christ with her tears, the sister of Martha and Lazarus and the mother of Jesus?

1282 *Shakespeare*

Hippolyta, Hermia and Helena are characters in which play?

1283 *Latin Terms*

Which two Latin words advise one to beware of the dog?

1284 *London*

Buckingham Palace stands at one end of the Mall; which building stands at the other end?

1285 *Geography*

Which African country on the Gulf of Guinea was formerly called the Gold Coast Colony?

1286 *History of Pop Music*

The 1960s pop group The Monkees reformed in 1996 and toured the UK and the USA. Name two of the four band members.

1287 *Phrases*

What does the Latin phrase *Fortis fortuna adiuvit* mean?

1288 *Twentieth-century Writers*

The detective Albert Campion was created by which English writer?

1289 *Britain*

Granted to the Scots in 945 AD, which city on the River Eden in the north-west of England is the only city to have been added to England since the Norman conquest?

1290 *Snooker*

Which of the colours is worth four points?

1291 *European Cities*

Which European city, the capital of Lombardy, is set in the heart of the Po Basin?

1292 *Politics*

Blackley, Gorton and Withington are parliamentary constituencies in which city?

1293 Coinage

'Pieces of eight' – a term beloved of writers of pirate stories – refers to the coinage of which country?

1294 The USA

Governors Island, Ellis Island and Liberty Island are small islands in the bay of which city?

1295 Food and Drink

In what everyday foodstuff would you find *Lactobacillus bulgarious*?

1296 Famous Quotations

Attributed to the American politician, Henry Kissinger, 'Power is the ultimate… ' what?

1297 History

What event took place in Westminster Abbey on Christmas Day, 1066?

1298 Nursery Rhymes

Which yellow-haired lover went to sea with silver buckles on his knee?

1299 Literature and Famous Writers

Which poet laureate wrote detective fiction under the pseudonym of Nicholas Blake?

1300 The USA

Who, in the USA, has the famous nickname the 'Comeback Kid'?

1301 British Flags

The first Union Flag of 1606 was a combination of the crosses of which two patron saints?

1302 Football

Manchester United play their home games at Old Trafford. Where do Manchester City play at home?

1303 Films of the 1990s

Which 1993 Steven Spielberg film ends with the actors, and the real-life characters they play, laying stones on the grave of the leading character?

1304 Geography

In which European country is the source of the River Rhine?

1305 *Politics*

On the Isle of Man, the House of Keys and the Legislative Council make up the parliament. What's that parliament called?

1306 *History*

Catherine of Braganza was his wife. Nell Gwynne was his famous mistress. Which is this seventeenth-century monarch?

1307 *English Law*

In English law, what are the two degrees of kindred, or relation by blood?

1308 *Education*

At which university in England is the final honours examination for a bachelor's degree called the Tripos?

1309 *Medicine*

What is the scientific or medical term for the art of midwifery?

1310 *Transport and Roads*

In the USA they are known as beltways; what do we call them in the UK?

1311 *Language*

What word, meaning 'great house', was used for the rulers of ancient Egypt?

1312 *Geography*

The monarch of which European country is Chief of State of the Faroe Islands?

1313 *History*

Who was executed at Fotheringhay Castle, Northamptonshire, in 1587?

1314 *European Cities*

In which European capital city are the Sibelius Memorial, the Sibelius Academy and the 1952 Olympic Stadium?

1315 *Newspapers*

Which national daily newspaper was founded in 1785 under the title *The Daily Universal Register*?

1316 *United Nations*

Which organ of the United Nations is based at The Peace Palace, The Hague?

1317 *Bonnie and Clyde*

What were the full names of Bonnie and Clyde?

1318 *The USA*

Which of the 50 state capital cities lies farthest south?

1319 *Currency*

The Greek drachma is made up of 100 what?

1320 *Geography*

What is the geographical name for the part of the Earth that lies above the 66 degree and 32 minute line of latitude?

1321 *Calendar*

What is the name of the Christian festival held on 6 January?

1322 *Geography*

What is the name of the group of 6554 islands that lies in the Gulf of Bothnia?

1323 *Television Writers*

Hancock's Half Hour and *Steptoe and Son* were written by which two writers?

1324 *Literature*

What family name connects the author of *Barchester Towers* and the author of *The Rector's Wife*?

1325 *United Nations*

How is the United Nations Development Fund for Women known for short?

1326 *Proverbs*

Complete this saying: 'A fool and his money…'

1327 *The UK*

In which Devon port is the Britannia Royal Naval College?

1328 *Geometry*

If a line is said to be normal to another, what does that mean?

1329 *The Arts*

In which field of the arts are Bill Kenwright, Michael Codron and Ray Cooney famous names?

1330 *Proverbs*

'Where ignorance is bliss…' what?

1331 *Chemistry*

Which metallic element has the highest melting point – 3410°C?

1332 *Medicine*

CVA or cerebrovascular accident is the medical term for what common occurrence?

1333 *Motor Racing*

What name is given to the area on a motor-racing circuit where refuelling and tyre changes take place?

1334 *Poetry*

'The Englishwoman', 'The Galloping Cat' and 'Not Waving But Drowning' are poems by which twentieth-century English writer?

1335 *Mythology*

The Phoenician Astarte and the Babylonian Ishtar are goddesses of what?

1336 *Scotland*

What is the Scottish Court of Chivalry called?

1337 *Motorways*

Which motorway crosses the north of England, from Merseyside to Humberside?

1338 *Currency*

Uganda, Kenya and Tanzania have official main units of currency with the same name. What is this name?

1339 *Nicknames*

Which European city is known as Diamond City?

1340 *The USA*

St Paul, Minnesota, St Louis, Missouri, Memphis, Tennessee and Baton Rouge, Louisiana. On which major river do all those cities stand?

1341 *Cricket*

How many days' play are scheduled in each county championship fixture?

1342 *Literary Families*

Edith and her brothers Sacheverell and Osbert: what is their surname?

1343 *Britain*

What was the name of the ancient track that crossed England from the Wash to Wiltshire, the section between Norfolk and Ivinghoe Beacon still much by walkers today?

1344 *Classical Music*

Piano Concerto in A minor, Norwegian Dances, the incidental music to *Peer Gynt*: who is the composer?

1345 *Proverbs*

'Birds are entangled by their feet, and men by their...' what?

1346 *Media*

In what field are Anne Swithinbank, Gay Search and Bob Flowerdew expert names?

1347 *Football*

The 'Blades' and the 'Owls' are the nicknames of the two football clubs from which city?

1348 *Language*

If something is described as navicular, what shape is it?

1349 *Monopoly*

On the Monopoly board there are two packs of cards. One pack is called Chance. What is the other pack called?

1350 *Science*

What is the fatty matter called that is derived from sheep's wool and is used as a base for emollients in cosmetics and shampoos?

1351 *Chess*

A chessman is any figure on a chessboard. What is a chess piece?

1352 *Natural History*

Pica pica is the Latin name for which common species of British bird?

1353 *Geography*

Which major city in the United Kingdom stands on the River Lagan?

1354 *Food and Drink*

What, in Indian cuisine, is garam masala?

1355 *British Cities*

In which English city are there open spaces called Midsummer Common, Parker's Piece and Jesus Green?

1356 *Shakespeare*

During which ancient historical event is *Troilus and Cressida* set?

1357 *History*

Which sixteenth-century king of England came to the throne at the age of nine, and died of tuberculosis at the age of 15?

1358 *Science*

What is the name of the American scientist, author and diplomat who demonstrated the electrical nature of lightning by flying a kite in a thunderstorm?

1359 *English Law*

How is the Latin phrase *thesaurus inventus* translated into English for legal purposes?

1360 *Botany*

By what name is the plant *Rosa canina* more commonly known?

1361 *Sport*

Ten years after the first University Boat Race, which other, now annual, event on the River Thames was first held in 1839?

1362 *Language*

For what two-word term is 'fax' an abbreviation?

1363 *Religion*

Jansenism was an extreme seventeenth to eighteenth century reform movement in which Christian church?

1364 *The UK*

At over 2900 feet, Pen-y-Fan is the highest point of which National Park in South Wales?

1365 *Organizations*

In which European city are the headquarters of OPEC, the Organization of the Petroleum Exporting Countries?

1366 *Shakespeare*

In *The Merchant of Venice*, which character in the play speaks of 'the quality of mercy'?

1367 Mythology

In which mythology is Odin the supreme ruler of the world?

1368 The British Isles

Hugh Town is the administrative centre of which group of islands?

1369 Geometry

How many lines of symmetry does a regular pentagon have?

1370 Measurement

A gill is what fraction of a pint?

1371 Astronomy

Which heavenly body, last sighted in 1985/86, is due again in 2061?

1372 Business Terms

Used by accountants, for example, what do the letters WIP stand for?

1373 Edinburgh

What name is given to the thoroughfare linking Edinburgh Castle and Holyrood Palace, made up of four streets that run into each other?

1374 Sport

In which sport are penalties awarded for hooking, spearing or slashing?

1375 House of Commons

What term applies to the unofficial system under which two MPs, one for each of the two major parties, agree to be absent from the Chamber for a particular vote?

1376 Science

Geodesy is the science concerned with the surveying and mapping of what?

1377 The Animal World

What name is given to the soft hairy skin that covers deers' antlers whilst growing?

1378 Food and Drink

Which state of southeast Mexico shares its name with a hot piquant sauce made from peppers and vinegar?

1379 Proverbs

'Don't change horses...' where?

1380 *Science*

Which part of an electric lightbulb transmits light by becoming white-hot?

1381 *Food and Drink*

What kind of dessert is a sachertorte?

1382 *Inventions*

Which British scientist invented the vacuum flask, in the 1890s?

1383 *Famous People*

In which English cathedral is Jane Austen buried?

1384 *The British Armed Forces*

Per Mare, Per Terram, meaning 'by sea, by land', is the motto of which branch of the Armed Forces?

1385 *Medicine*

Dysphagia is difficulty in doing what?

1386 *Geography*

Which European capital city lies on the Manzanares River?

1387 *Shipping*

Referring to the cargo capacity of a merchant ship, what is usually abbreviated to DWT?

1388 *Counties*

Oakham is the administrative centre of which newly re-established county?

1389 *Foreign Phrases*

What is the meaning of the French phrase *nuit blanche*, meaning 'white night'?

1390 *Abbreviations*

In international trade agreements, for example, what do the initials MFN mean?

1391 *Poetry*

'A thing of beauty is a joy for ever'. Who was the poet who wrote this line?

1392 *Opera*

Rossini and Massenet both wrote operas based on the same fairy tale by French author, Charles Perrault. Which fairy tale?

1393 Science

The ore galena is the chief source for which metal?

1394 Italy

Of which autonomous Italian region is Turin the capital?

1395 Business

For what is CIF an abbreviation?

1396 Television

Which American detective series of the 1970s launched the careers of Jaclyn Smith, Farrah Fawcett, Kate Jackson and, later, Cheryl Ladd?

1397 Shakespeare

What is the name of Hamlet's mother, who is married to her late husband's brother?

1398 The English Monarchy

Who was the husband of Mary I of England?

1399 The Monarchy

Victoria of Saxe-Coburg-Saalfeld was the mother of which British monarch?

1400 The Peerage

In the UK, which title ranks below an earl, but above a baron?

15 to 1

ROUND THREE
Questions

1401 *History*

In 1916 a woman called Wallis Warfield married a man called Earl Winfield Spencer. In 1928 she married Ernest Simpson. Who, in 1937, was her third husband?

1402 *The Bible*

Genesis chapter 28, verse 12: 'He dreamed, and behold a ladder set up on the earth and the top of it reached to heaven: and behold the angels of God ascending and descending on it.' Whose ladder?

1403 *The UK*

A direct flight from Norwich in Norfolk to Maidstone in Kent would cross which two intervening counties?

1404 *Medicine*

What is the branch of surgery, anaplasty, more commonly called?

1405 *History of Medicine*

What in the 1920s was the first antibiotic to be discovered?

1406 *English Poetry*

'Water, water everywhere/And all the boards did shrink/Water, water everywhere/Nor any drop to drink'. These are lines from which poem?

1407 *History of Medicine*

In 1796 Edward Jenner, a Gloucestershire doctor, made the first successful vaccination against which disease?

1408 *Fairy Tales*

In which Grimm's fairy tale does a mysterious dwarf spin straw into gold for the miller's daughter, in return for her first-born child?

1409 *History*

He was born at Schloss Rosenau near Coburg in 1819, and died 42 years later at Windsor in Berkshire. Who was he?

1410 *The UK*

Which cathedral city, and former capital of the Anglo-Saxon kingdom of Wessex, lies on the River Itchen in Hampshire?

1411 *The USA*

Henry and William were two Americans who, in the mid-1800s, set up a carrier service between Buffalo and the West: what were their surnames?

1412 *History of Sport*

Which British former Wimbledon singles champion became, in 1982, the first woman to be elected to the All England Committee?

1413 *Geography*

Which group of islands in the North Atlantic, part of the Kingdom of Shetland, lie north-west of the Shetlands and southeast of Iceland?

1414 *The Olympics*

Which American city will host the 2002 Winter Olympics?

1415 *The Bible*

What is the Octateuch?

1416 *History of Food*

Which American pioneered the method of deep-freezing food?

1417 *Famous Inscriptions*

'Give me your tired, your poor, your huddled masses': on what can that famous inscription be found?

1418 *Business Terms*

What two-word expression describes the approach, often by telephone, made by a salesperson to a prospective buyer, where no previous contact has been made?

1419 *Alphabets*

Tango, Uniform, Victor. What comes next?

1420 *Airports*

Norman Manley International airport serves the capital city of which Caribbean Commonwealth country?

1421 *Names*

By what general name is the larva of the furniture beetle known, which bores holes in dead timber and causes considerable damage to old furniture?

1422 *Terms and Phrases*

Which Chinese term meaning 'wind water' is given to the belief that arrangement and orientation are affected by energy flow, and should be taken into account when designing and furnishing buildings?

1423 *The Financial World*

What two-word expression is used to describe shares in large and well-established companies that are regarded as particularly safe investments?

1424 *Science*

Which metallic element has the chemical symbol Na?

1425 *Mnemonics*

'Richard of York gave battle in vain' is a mnemonic used to remind one of what?

1426 *Animal Stars*

What is the name of the Alsatian dog found in France during World War One, who later became Hollywood's first animal film star?

1427 *Words and Phrases*

What name is given to the personification of death in the form of a cloaked skeleton wielding a large scythe?

1428 *Politics*

In which decade were Winston Churchill, Anthony Eden and Harold Macmillan all Prime Minister?

1429 *Newspapers*

Principally published in New York, what is the American equivalent of the UK's *Financial Times*?

1430 *Television*

Pennies from Heaven, The Singing Detective and *Lipstick on your Collar* were all written by which celebrated dramatist?

1431 *The UK*

In which town in the northwest of England are the 300-acre Stanley Park, the 40-acre Pleasure Beach and a famous construction, built in 1894, resembling one in Paris?

1432 *Proverbs*

If you run after two hares what will happen?

1433 *Food and Drink*

Literally meaning 'before the pasta', what Italian term is used to refer to hot or cold hors d'oeuvres?

1434 *Historical Nicknames*

The eighteenth-century architect and landscape gardener Lancelot Brown was popularly known by what nickname?

1435 *Science*

What is the name of the curved upper surface of a liquid in a tube?

1436 *Cartoon Characters*

What is the name of the work-shy Geordie, created by Reg Smythe, who with his wife Flo first appeared in the *Daily Mirror* in the 1950s?

1437 *South Africa*

Chief Buthelezi is a leader of which people?

1438 *Food and Drink*

Fino, Amontillado and Oloroso are varieties of which fortified wine?

1439 *Song Lines*

Complete this verse from the Ira Gershwin song: 'The way you wear your hat,/The way you sip your tea,/The mem'ry of all that/No, no!...'

1440 *Classical Music*

What name is given to a musical composition, most usually a slow piano piece, that suggests the romantic beauty of the night?

1441 *Awards*

What connection is there between the Nobel Peace Prize awarded to Dag Hammarskjöld, an Oscar to Peter Finch and the VC awarded to Colonel H. Jones in the Falklands?

1442 *Computing*

What peripheral device, used for moving a cursor about on a VDU, could be described as either mechanical or optical?

1443 *Modern Quotations*

From the physicist, Stephen Hawking: 'Someone told me that each equation I included in the book would halve the sales.' Which best-selling book?

1444 *American Literature*

Which famous novel by Louisa M. Alcott tells the story of Mrs March and her four daughters, whilst her husband is away in the Civil War?

1445 *Science*

What term is commonly used to refer to a quantity of distance that is so large it cannot be counted or measured and is represented by a symbol resembling a figure eight on its side?

1446 *British Organizations*

Members of one of the charitable foundations of the Most Venerable Order of the Hospital of St John of Jerusalem may often be seen at football matches and pop concerts. How are they better known?

1447 *The UK*

Which castle in West Sussex is the home of the Dukes of Norfolk?

1448 *Australia*

The name Australia is derived from the Latin *australis*, which means what?

1449 *Science Fiction*

Which famous science fiction film was based on 'The Sentinel', a short story by Arthur C. Clarke?

1450 *Inventions*

What aids to road safety, invented by Percy Shaw, were first laid in a road near Bradford in 1934?

1451 *Science/Physics*

Which unit of heat is approximately equivalent to 4.2 joules?

1452 *Literature*

What is the name of Samuel Johnson's eighteenth-century biographer?

1453 *Fictional Characters*

Which Chinese master criminal was created in 1913 by the writer Sax Rohmer, and has been played on film by Warner Oland, Boris Karloff, Henry Brandon, Christopher Lee and Peter Sellers?

1454 *The Bible*

Who first appears in the Bible in Genesis as the son of Lamech and ninth in descent from Adam?

1455 *Famous Scientific Principles*

The weight of the liquid displaced by a floating body is equal to the weight of the body. Whose principle?

1456 *Mathematics*

Which branch of mathematics deals with the abstract investigation of the properties of numbers by means of symbols?

1457 *Theatre*

What word describes a play or scene acted out with gestures but not speech?

1458 *Cricketing Legends*

Which famous Gloucestershire cricketer played his last first-class game in 1908, at the age of 60?

1459 *Music and Inventions*

Which instrument was patented in 1846 following its inventor's attempts to improve the bass clarinet?

1460 *Greek Mythology*

What is the name of the instrument or weapon held by Poseidon, god of the sea?

1461 *Food and Drink*

What name is given to the proprietary brand of bitters, named after a town on the Orinoco River in Venezuela?

1462 *The UK*

Teignmouth, Torquay and Paignton are on the coast of which county?

1463 *Opera*

Verdi's opera *Nabucco* tells the story of which biblical king?

1464 *Classic Television*

Which classic television programme featured two crotchety old men, Statler and Waldorf, who heckled constantly from their position in the box seats?

1465 *The English Monarchy*

The nickname of which eleventh-century king is derived from his extreme piety?

1466 *Ranks and Insignia*

Which rank of the British Army is signified by three 'pips' worn on each shoulder?

1467 *History of London*

What, until 1783, were held near the site in London now occupied by Marble Arch and marked by a plaque at the junctions of Edgware and Bayswater Roads?

1468 *Cartography*

On British Ordnance Survey maps the two grid references are known as northings and what else?

1469 *Science*

Which term or word can mean both the oxidation of metal, and fungi which cause diseases of cereal grains?

1470 *Football Facts*

What links the football world cup winners of 1930, 1934, 1966, 1974, 1978 and 1998?

1471 *American Writers*

Ken Kesey's best-known novel, later a film starring Jack Nicholson, was based on his experiences as a ward attendant in a mental hospital. What is its title?

1472 *Food and Drink*

Which breakfast dish consists of rice, flaked fish and hard-boiled eggs?

1473 *European Literature*

In which Thomas Mann story, later a film starring Dirk Bogarde, does Gustav von Aschenbach stay in an Italian city in spite of a cholera epidemic?

1474 *Geography*

Which of the world's oceans includes the Red Sea, the Persian Gulf and the Bay of Bengal?

1475 *English Law*

What is the CPS?

1476 *The UK*

The rivers Wensum, Wissey and Yare all flow through which county in the east of England?

1477 *Words and Phrases*

If something has a low priority, where, according to the phrase, would you place it on the stove?

1478 *Quotations*

From *The Wind in the Willows*: 'Glorious stirring sight!... The poetry of motion, the real way to travel... O bliss! O poop poop! O my! O my!' What was Toad getting so excited about?

1479 *Borders*

The island of Borneo comprises parts or all of three countries: what are names of two of them?

1480 *Geography*

Which Scottish term for a coastal area of sand dunes, supporting coarse grass and low shrubs, has become so synonymous with the game of golf that it is often used as a term for a golf course?

1481 *Birds*

What is the common name of the *Mimus polyglottus* of North America, a songbird noted for its mimicry of the calls and songs of other birds?

1482 *The English Monarchy*

Catherine of Aragon (the first wife of Henry VIII) was the mother of which English monarch?

1483 *The British Monarchy*

George III, George IV and William IV ruled Britain in which century?

1484 *American Politics*

Prior to Bill Clinton, who was the last Democrat President of the United States?

1485 *Building Developments*

What is the name of the unusual model town constructed in 1968 in Billund, Denmark?

1486 *Card Games*

Which card game, with a French name meaning railway, developed from baccarat and is popularly known as chemmy or shimmy?

1487 *The Church of England*

Frederick Coggan, John Habgood and David Hope have all held which office during the past 25 years?

1488 *History and Roads*

The present-day A5 follows much of the route of the Roman road that linked London and Chester. What is its name?

1489 *Medicine*

A form of paraesthesia, what name is commonly given to the tingling sensation of the limbs when numbness begins to wear off?

1490 *Art and Literature*

What nationality by birth were the writer Georges Simenon (creator of Maigret), the surrealist painter René Magritte, and the composer César Franck?

1491 *Wales*

Which thirteenth-century castle in Gwynedd, on the coast of Cardigan Bay, now part of a World Heritage Site, is sometimes called the Castle of Lost Causes because it was defended so many times to no avail?

1492 *Twentieth-century Literature*

In the volatile political and religious atmosphere of late seventeenth-century New England, Abigail Williams accuses her former employer of witchcraft: in which play by Arthur Miller?

1493 *Classical Music*

What name is given to Haydn's Symphony no. 94 because of a sudden loud drumbeat in the slow movement?

1494 *Ancient History*

In which present-day North African country are the ruins of Rome's rival, Carthage?

1495 *Science*

What two-word term describes the lowest hypothetical temperature on the Kelvin scale, at which all molecular activity ceases?

1496 *Advertising*

Which men's aftershave lotion, made by Fabergé, has been promoted over the years by Henry Cooper, Paul Gascoigne, Daley Thompson and Kevin Keegan to prove that it was not unmanly to 'splash it all over'?

1497 *Sports Events*

In which activity is 'mad Sunday' a major event held annually on the Isle of Man?

1498 *Veterinary Science*

What sort of animals are particularly affected by an infectious and contagious disease known as strangles?

1499 *The Cinema*

Barbra Streisand made her Oscar-winning Hollywood debut in the film version of which musical, based on the life of the comedienne Fanny Brice?

1500 *British Towns*

Which English town changed hands between the Scots and the English at least 13 times between the twelfth and fifteenth centuries and has a football team that plays in the Scottish League?

1501 *Sport and Politics*

What is the name of the famous British athlete who retired from the sport in 1990 to pursue a career in politics and later became the MP for Falmouth and Camborne?

1502 *Film Stars*

What is the name of the legendary Swedish-born film star, who died in 1990, and who was finally laid to rest in 1999 in the Stockholm cemetery where her family are buried?

1503 *The Bible*

In Matthew 27, verses 57 to 60, who went to Pilate and asked for the body of Jesus and buried it in his own tomb?

1504 *James Bond Films*

A View to a Kill was the last film with which actor playing James Bond?

1505 *Quotations*

Who in the *Oxford Dictionary of Modern Quotations* has the two entries 'Seriously, though, he's doing a grand job,' and 'Hello, good evening and welcome'?

1506 *The American West*

In which incident in the history of the Wild West did Frank and Tom McLaury and Billy Clanton die at Tombstone, Arizona in 1881?

1507 *Musicals*

In which Lerner and Loewe musical are there characters called Arthur, Guinevere, Lancelot, Mordred and Merlin?

1508 *The Swinging Sixties*

The actress and singer Lesley Lawson was a world-famous model in the 1960s. By what name was she known then?

1509 *Pop Music*

'Careless Whisper', 'Jesus to a Child' and 'Fastlove' were all British number one hits for which singer?

1510 *Common Expressions*

Which two-word expression describes an addition to a house to accommodate an elderly parent?

1511 *Theatre*

Which great British actor and director played Romeo, Hamlet, Macbeth and Henry V in the 1930s, Richard III, Hotspur and King Lear in the 1940s, Antony, Titus Andronicus and Malvolio in the 1950s, Othello in the 1960s and Shylock in the 1970s?

1512 *Weights and Measures*

Which imperial measurement is equal to 1609 kilometres?

1513 *World Wars One and Two*

What is the significance of the dates 6 April 1917 and 8 December 1941?

1514 *Geography*

Cape Comorin is the southernmost tip of which Asian country?

1515 *Classical Music*

The Hallelujah Chorus is part of which larger choral work by Handel?

1516 *Astronomy*

What term is used to describe the partial or total disappearance from view of an astronomical object when it passes directly behind another?

1517 *Geography*

Of the cities in the world that have an urban population of over 10 million, two of them are in India. Which two?

1518 *Words*

Where would a troglodyte live?

1519 *Classic Television*

The Fish Slapping Dance, the Lumberjack Song and the Ministry of Silly Walks were performed by which famous comedy team?

1520 *H.G. Wells*

In which novel does the central character become temporarily stranded in the year 802,701?

1521 *Technology*

What is the three-dimensional image created by a split laser beam called?

1522 *Science*

Petrology is the study of the origins and composition of what?

1523 *Name Connections*

What word connects a breed of heavy draught horse and a bank based in Scotland?

1524 *Geography*

Name the stretch of water that divides the southern tip of the Iberian Peninsula and Morocco?

1525 *Children's Literature*

What nationality was Hans Christian Andersen?

1526 *Word Connections*

What word connects a letter in the Greek alphabet, and a flat area at the mouth of some major rivers?

1527 *Mathematics*

What name is given to any four-sided plane figure in which the opposite sides are equal in length?

1528 *The Commonwealth*

Two Commonwealth countries are islands in the Mediterranean Sea. Name one of them.

1529 *Medicine*

Kleptomania is a psychological disorder in which a person has an irresistible compulsion to do what?

1530 *American Literature*

What was the sequel to Mark Twain's *The Adventures of Tom Sawyer*?

1531 *Science*

What word describes the conversion of a liquid to a gas?

1532 *Mythology*

What is the name of the winged horse of Greek mythology?

1533 *Charles Dickens*

Who had been the late Jacob Marley's business partner in a Dickens novel?

1534 *The UK*

There are two established or state Churches in the United Kingdom. The Church of England is one, what is the other?

1535 *Music*

Which instrument, widely used in Asian music, has a name coming from the Persian meaning 'three-stringed'?

1536 *Food and Drink*

What Italian name is given to coffee made by topping espresso with the creamy foam and liquid of steamed milk, dusted with chocolate or cinnamon?

1537 *Quotations*

'Four legs good, two legs bad' is a quotation from which George Orwell novel?

1538 *Geometry*

What name is given to a cord that divides a circle into equal parts?

1539 *Geography*

Edmonton is the capital of which Canadian province?

1540 *Measurements*

How many carats in pure gold?

1541 *Geography*

What range of hills run along the English–Scottish border?

1542 *Latin Terms*

What is meant by the Latin *Fidei defensor*?

1543 *Art*

What term is used in art to describe paintings containing only objects, often domestic but sometimes skulls, dead game etc., viewed close up?

1544 *Mythology*

In which mythology are Isis and Osiris the parents of the god Horus?

1545 *Word Connections*

Which word connects a small village and the title of a Shakespeare play?

1546 *Music*

What Japanese term meaning 'empty orchestra' is used to refer to a pre-recorded backing track to which members of the public sing the words?

1547 *Motor Vehicle Registration*

Which letter is the international registration letter for Spain?

1548 *The Armed Forces*

Officially, who appoints commissioned officers in the armed forces?

1549 *Sport*

Which event takes its name from the Greek words meaning 'ten' and 'contest'?

1550 *Computing*

What term is used for a diagram that shows the arrangement of the steps of a process or program?

1551 *Religion*

What is the tall pointed head-dress worn by Roman Catholic and Anglican bishops called?

1552 *The USA*

What is the name of the official Presidential retreat, situated in Maryland?

1553 *Sayings*

Upon whose tomb in Westminster Abbey is the text: 'They buried him among the kings because he had done good toward God and toward his house'?

1554 *Language*

Which French phrase meaning 'on an equal basis' is used in English to refer to a young person who receives little or no payment but board and lodgings in return for their work?

1555 *Ancient Rome*

Of the four main types of gladiator that took part in combat, what was the *retiarius* armed with to ensnare his opponent?

1556 *Dentistry*

What popular name is given to the last molar, top and bottom, on both sides of each jaw?

1557 *English Law*

What is the Latin term for a writ obliging a person to appear before a court?

1558 *Aviation*

What is the national carrier of Australia?

1559 *Sport*

What term is used in various sports for a stroke, shot or kick at a moving ball before it hits the ground?

1560 *British History*

What name is given to the priests of the pre-Christian Celtic religion?

1561 Animals

What was the name of London Zoo's first ever male elephant, who arrived in 1867 with his mate Alice, and immediately gave his name to anything of large size?

1562 Children's Literature

How are the Beverley children, Edward, Humphrey, Alice and Edith, described in the title of a famous historical children's story by Captain Marryat?

1563 Geography

What term is used to describe either of the two annual occasions when the sun is exactly above the equator and day and night are of equal length?

1564 Classical Music

By what name is Chopin's short piece 'Opus 64 No. 1 for Piano' better known?

1565 Festivals

Which festival has a French name meaning 'fat Tuesday'?

1566 Geography

What was known by the British, until 1865, as Peak XV, until it was renamed after a British Surveyor-General of India?

1567 History of Pop

With which group, formerly disbanded but now re-formed, was Boy George the lead singer when it had hits in the early 1980s including 'Karma Chameleon'?

1568 Europe

Which is the largest island that is part of the continent of Europe?

1569 The Animal World

What is the distinguishing feature of a Manx cat?

1570 Quotations

To whom was Keith Richards reputedly referring when he said, 'You don't have to, you know, prance around and run five miles round a stadium in a poofy football suit to prove anything. There's no point in pretending to be Peter Pan'?

1571 *Sport*

In which sport are the competitors identified by their racing jackets bearing the trap number and colours?

1572 *The Royal Family*

She died at Marlborough House in London on 24 March 1953, 17 years after her husband had died at Sandringham in 1936. Who was she?

1573 *History*

On which island in the Pacific did the *Bounty* mutineer, Fletcher Christian, found his colony after leaving Tahiti?

1574 *Rock Music*

Which veteran rock musician and singer is known as Van the Man?

1575 *Scotland*

What is the name of the orange-coloured fizzy soft drink famously advertised with the slogan 'made in Scotland from girders'?

1576 *Tennis*

Which Czech-born tennis player played 132 singles matches at Wimbledon from 1973 to 1994, losing only 13 of them?

1577 *English Food*

What name, from an English county, is given to the savoury turnover comprising a chopped meat-and-potato filling, sometimes with vegetables, within a pastry case?

1578 *Language*

Frame, ridge and dome are all common types of what?

1579 *Insurance*

What name is given to the temporary document that an insurance company issues to someone with whom it has a contract until the policy has been drawn up and delivered?

1580 *The Animal World*

What word is used to describe animals that feed mainly on meat?

1581 *Cartoon Characters*

Who is Popeye's girlfriend?

1582 *Meteorology*

A barography is used for recording variations in what, specifically?

1583 *Arthurian Legend*

What was the name of the capital of Arthur's kingdom?

1584 *Athletics*

In which throwing event are the greatest distances achieved?

1585 *Europe*

Which small country, a member of the European Union, is sandwiched in between Belgium, France and Germany?

1586 *Medicine*

What is a physician who specializes in children's diseases called?

1587 *Children's Literature*

In *One Hundred and One Dalmatians*, what kind of animal is Sergeant Tibbs?

1588 *Literature*

Who wrote *Catch 22*?

1589 *Mental Arithmetic*

What is the sum of half a dozen, a dozen and a baker's dozen?

1590 *Europe*

If you sailed due east from Wick in the north of Scotland, in which country would your next landfall be?

1591 *Chemistry*

If a chemical reaction is described as aerobic, what, specifically, is involved?

1592 *Mathematics*

How is the value of pi expressed as a vulgar fraction?

1593 *Science*

What is the name of the device that measures the height of an aircraft above sea level?

1594 *Theatre*

The Royal National Theatre in London comprises three theatres. Name two of the three.

1595 The USA

In which century was George Washington President of the United States?

1596 History of the Fourteenth Century

Charles the Fair, Charles the Wise and Charles the Mad were fourteenth-century kings in which European country?

1597 Mythology

In Greek mythology, who asked Oedipus the riddle: 'Which is the animal that has four feet in the morning, two at midday and three in the evening?'

1598 American History

At what period of his office might an American president be called a 'lame-duck President'?

1599 The UK

At which major event in May 1997 might you have encountered Lord Byro, Miss Moneypenny, Ronnie the Rhino and the Space Age Superhero from Planet Beanus?

1600 Mythology

Which Greek youth, having fallen in love with his own reflection in a pool, pined away and died, a flower bearing his name growing upon the spot?

1601 Words

Which Italian word, from the Latin meaning 'not known', is used to mean an assumed identity, or having one's true identity concealed?

1602 The Geography of London

What, in London, are the Westbourne, the Effra and the Tyburn?

1603 Names and Colours

Which colour links a unit of British marine commandos, paper currency in the USA and antiquated fire engines?

1604 Frank Sinatra

For his role as Angelo Maggio, in which film did Frank Sinatra win an Oscar as Best Supporting Actor?

1605 *Religion*

Enoch's father was the first murderer in the Bible; his uncle was the first victim. Who, therefore, were his father and uncle?

1606 *Science/Music*

A needle or stylus is used to read the information on a vinyl record. What is used, in the same sense, to read the information on a compact disc?

1607 *Geography*

Where are the Puerto Rico Trench, the South Sandwich Trench and the Romanche Trench?

1608 *Prime Ministers*

Who was the British prime minister at the turn of the 1920s into the 1930s?

1609 *Science/Astronomy*

'An astronomical object so dense that not even light can escape its gravitational field.' What phenomenon is this a description of?

1610 *Ships and the Sea*

What type of ancient vessel was a 'trireme'?

1611 *Famous Last Words*

'Farewell, my friends, I go to glory' were the last words of which famous dancer, before a fatal accident that was caused when her scarf got caught in the wheel of a car in which she was travelling?

1612 *Shakespeare*

In *Hamlet*, the skull of Yorick is dug up, while a grave is being prepared for whom?

1613 *Pre-decimal Currency*

How many old pennies made a crown?

1614 *International Football*

Two players share the honour of scoring the most goals for Scotland in international matches. Name one of the two.

1615 *Sayings*

'Don't spoil the ship for…' what?

1616 *Films*

In which Oscar-winning movie did the death of the racehorse Khartoum make cinema-goers the world over gasp?

1617 *BBC Radio*

The world's longest-running radio drama was first broadcast on 1 January 1951 and featured Harry Oakes and Gwen Berryman playing husband and wife Dan and Doris. What was the programme?

1618 *Science*

Why are odorants TBM and DMS added to natural gas supplies?

1619 *Television*

Especially used in sport, what in television terms is an OB?

1620 *The USA*

In which decade of the nineteenth century did the American Civil War take place?

1621 *History of Medicine*

Why is 3 December 1967 a famous date in medical history?

1622 *Shakespeare*

Which eponymous character in a Shakespeare tragedy speaks these lines: 'I am a very foolish, fond old man, Fourscore and upward, not an hour more or less, And, to deal plainly, I fear I am not in perfect mind'?

1623 *Musicals*

Which film musical, starring Howard Keel, was adapted from Stephen Vincent Benét's short story 'The Sobbin' Women', which in turn was 'inspired' by the classical tale of the rape of the Sabine women?

1624 *Classic Television*

Intoned by the judge at the beginning of each episode, what was the full name of the character played by Ronnie Barker in *Porridge*?

1625 *Memorials*

In France it is at the foot of the Arc de Triomphe in Paris, in America at Arlington Cemetery, in the UK it is in Westminster Abbey. What is it?

1626 *Sport*

Which two football teams play against each other in what is called the 'Old Firm' Derby?

1627 *Marine Life*

What is described as a hard stony substance secreted by certain aquatic invertebrates as an external skeleton, typically forming large reefs in warm seas?

1628 *American Presidents*

Ronald Reagan was the first US president to have been the head of a trade union. From 1947 to 1960 he was president of an organization called the SAG, representing whom?

1629 *Famous Political Quotations*

Margot Asquith famously said of David Lloyd George: 'He can't see a belt without…' what?

1630 *The USA*

The state of Wyoming has the nickname the 'Equality State'. Why?

1631 *The Animal World*

What is the distinguishing feature of the Rhodesian hunting dog that gives it its name?

1632 *The UK*

The house was originally called Alveton Lodge and was once the home of the Earls of Shrewsbury. In 1924 it was sold to a private company and opened to the public. By what name is this theme park, 15 miles east of Stoke-on-Trent, now known?

1633 *Science*

What name is given in engineering to a block of iron, which supports work during forging, and in anatomy to a bone in the middle ear?

1634 *Literary Dynasties*

Which literary dynasty has so far produced a record four generations of authors, with nine writers publishing 150 books over a period of 111 years – the most prolific and bestselling being Alec and Evelyn respectively?

1635 *Products*

For which product is the Sicilian town of Marsala best known?

1636 *Famous People*

What is the name of the English animal conservationist and painter – a founding member of the World Wildlife Fund and the founder of the Wildfowl Trust at Slimbridge, Gloucestershire?

1637 *Chemicals*

Which gas is used to fill balloons and airships because it is lighter than air and, unlike hydrogen, does not burn?

1638 *The Commonwealth*

Which Asian country joined the Commonwealth on its creation in 1947, left in 1972, and then rejoined in 1989?

1639 *Europe*

What is the name of the spring at Vergeze, southwest of Nîmes in southern France that gives its name to an effervescent natural mineral water sold throughout the world?

1640 *Government*

The Fire Service College and the UK Passport Agency are executive agencies of which government department?

1641 *Words and Phrases*

Rejecting the essential with the inessential. What phrase, which involves a tiny child and some dirty soapy water, is used for this?

1642 *History of the Middle Ages*

Henry V led the English army to victory over French forces at Agincourt on 25 October of which year?

1643 *Legend*

Which European hero refused to bow to a hat erected upon a pole by the Austrian Duke's steward, and was forced as punishment to perform a now-famous feat involving his son?

1644 *History of Medicine*

Which disease was once commonly called 'consumption'?

1645 *The UK*

What, in the early and middle twentieth century, were the Camden Town Group and the Euston Road School?

1646 *Phrases*

What phrase, used as the title of a 1975 film starring David Niven, means a person or object that appears threatening but is actually weak and powerless?

1647 *Architecture*

With which European city was the Art Nouveau architect Antoni Gaudi chiefly associated?

1648 *Children's Literature*

An east wind blows a mysterious woman out of the sky to number seventeen Cherry Tree Lane, where she is hired as a nanny for the Banks children. What is the novel?

1649 *Geography*

If you sailed due west from anywhere on the west coast of Ireland, in which country would your next continental landfall be?

1650 *People*

She was born Isabella Mary Mayson in 1836, but is best remembered for a domestic manual written in her married name and published in 1861. What was this name?

1651 *Medicine*

If a substance is described as cytotoxic, what does it harm, specifically?

1652 *Astronomy*

Which word in astronomy means the elliptical path through space of one celestial body around another?

1653 *Film Facts*

Which American, with a film released in 1984, became the first woman to write, produce, direct, sing and star in a film?

1654 *Famous Voyages*

What is the name of the log raft on which Norwegian adventurer Thor Heyerdahl and five other men sailed from Peru to Polynesia in 1947?

1655 *English Literature*

Which epic poem is the sequel to *Paradise Lost*?

1656 *History of the USA*

What did the Dutchman Peter Minuit buy in 1626 for trinkets valued at some 60 guilders?

1657 *Music*

'Symphony No. 101 in D' by Haydn is given a nickname because of the tick-tock rhythm of the slow movement. What is the nickname?

1658 *Geography*

The two Russian rivers, the Ural and the Volga, both empty into which landlocked body of water?

1659 *History*

By what name had the Garden Tower at the Tower of London become known by the Tudor period?

1660 *Medicine*

Which organs of the body are affected by the condition pulmonary emphysema?

1661 *Boxing*

In the legendary boxing match held in Zaire in 1974, nicknamed the 'Rumble in the Jungle', who did Muhammed Ali defeat to win back the world heavyweight crown?

1662 *Literature*

The eponymous villain of which James Bond novel and film had the first name Auric?

1663 *Medicine*

Which of the five senses is measured by an esthesiometer?

1664 *Name Connections*

What name connects a nineteenth-century German statesman and the state capital of North Dakota?

1665 *The Royal Family*

What relation is Prince Charles to Queen Victoria?

1666 *Literary Characters*

What is the name of the elegant, noble detective created by Dorothy L. Sayers?

1667 *Science*

What is the name given to the chemical reaction in which the action of water breaks down a substance into smaller molecules?

1668 *Song Lines*

Complete this verse from an Ira Gershwin song:
'I got rhythm, I got music, I got my man…'

1669 *History of the USA*

Who was assassinated in Memphis, Tennessee, in April 1968?

1670 *The British Isles*

Sanday, Stronsay and Westray are three of the 21 islands of which group of islands?

1671 *Geography*

A Cairene is a native or citizen of which capital city?

1672 *Dance*

The name of which Spanish dance, in quick two-four time, literally means double step?

1673 *Famous Quotations*

'Mad, bad and dangerous to know' is a comment on Lord Byron by whom?

1674 *Place Names*

A town in North Wales shares its name with the pool where Jesus healed a lame man in St John's Gospel. What is its name?

1675 *Opera*

Marcello, Musetta and Mimi appear in which Puccini opera?

1676 *Religious Movements*

What name was given to the worldwide religious revivalist movement founded by American evangelist Dr Frank Buchman in the 1930s?

1677 *Politics*

Since 1895, which country has been ruled successively by a Khedive, a Sultan, a King and a President?

1678 *Literary Expressions*

In an epistolary novel, what form does the narrative take?

1679 *History of London*

Which Lord Mayor of London, in the fifteenth century, bequeathed the money to help found the Guildhall Library?

1680 *Foreign Phrases*

What French phrase implies that the privilege of rank imposes obligations?

1681 *Geography*

Which country has six time zones, ranging from five to ten hours behind Greenwich Mean Time?

1682 *Theatre*

Which black comedy by Joseph Kesselring, later a film, involves the elderly Brewster sisters, who cure the loneliness of gentleman callers by murdering them with poisoned elderberry wine?

1683 *The USA*

Four of the states of the USA begin with the word 'new'. New Jersey and New Mexico are two of them. What are the other two?

1684 *Geography*

The landlocked African country of Lesotho is completely surrounded by one other country. Which one?

1685 *Medicine*

What sort of creature is *Hirudo medicinalis* and how was it used in medicine?

1686 *Wars and Battles*

Prestonpans and Falkirk were two battles during the 1745 Jacobite rebellions. Which was the third and final decisive battle of this campaign?

1687 *Retailing*

What name is given to the identification system that consists of a printed pattern of lines and spaces, which record such information as batch and price numbers, and can be read by a cash register?

1688 *Geography*

The Strait of Malacca separates which large Indonesian island from the Malay peninsula?

1689 *Geography*

What in Antarctica have the names Nimrod, Slessor and Scott?

1690 *Hobbies*

If you went out with some gentles, a jig, a gag and a coop what would you be going to do?

1691 *Agriculture*

What crop is produced in Asia by farming the swamp grass *Oryza sativa*?

1692 *London*

Which famous toy store on Regent Street is named after its founder, who came to London and opened a shop called 'Noah's Ark'?

1693 *Roman Britain*

The Roman name of which town, north-west of London, was Verulamium?

1694 *Art and Artists*

What is the surname of the famous brother and sister painters, Augustus and Gwen?

1695 *Opera*

Which fairy tale by the Brothers Grimm was turned into an opera by the German composer Engelbert Humperdink?

1696 *World War One*

Which British poet, an officer in the Royal Naval Division, died en route to the Dardenelles in April 1915, and was buried on the Greek island of Skyros?

1697 *Africa*

From independence in 1960 until 1971 it was known as the Congo; since 1997 it has been officially called the Democratic Republic of Congo. By what name was it known in the intervening years?

1698 *Sport*

In which town in Warwickshire is there a public school that gives its name to a sport?

1699 *Bingo Calling*

What was the origin of the bingo call 'Seven and six, was she worth it'?

1700 *Language*

What sort of speech is a valedictory speech?

1701 *Modern Art*

The portrait of the late Ossie Clark, with his wife Celia and pet Percy and the painting *The Bigger Splash* are well-known works by which Yorkshire-born artist?

1702 *Theatre*

In which Oscar Wilde play does the heroine ask for the head of a prophet, in return for dancing for the King?

1703 *Chemistry*

Which chemical element has the symbol Kr?

1704 *Twentieth-century Music*

Which Russian composer wrote the pieces *Elegy for JFK* and *In Memoriam Dylan Thomas*?

1705 *Nursery Rhymes*

When did the Queen of Hearts make some tarts?

1706 *Politics*

What, traditionally, is the origin of the specific distance between the two red lines that run down the centre of the Chamber of the House of Commons between the Government and Opposition front benches?

1707 *Terms and Phrases*

A numismatist is an expert on coins, what does a notaphilist study?

1708 *Counties*

In which county are the Vale of Pewsy, the Marlborough Downs and Salisbury Plain?

1709 *Latin Terms*

Nolens volens is the Latin version of which common expression?

1710 *Detective Fiction*

Dashiell Hammett's most famous character was introduced in his novel *The Maltese Falcon* and played by Humphrey Bogart in a film of the book. What was his name?

1711 *Chemistry*

Ascorbic acid is another name for which vitamin?

1712 *Geography*

What word describes any two places that are on diametrically opposite sides of the globe?

1713 *Geography*

When Venice was a republic it was styled La Serenissima. Which present-day small European country, the oldest state in Europe, calls itself 'The Most Serene Republic'?

1714 *Cities*

Which English cathedral city grew from an early Anglo-Saxon settlement near the confluence of the rivers Yare and Wensum?

1715 *Royal Quotes*

Which member of the royal family is reported to have said, 'My favourite programme is *Mrs Dale's Diary*. I try never to miss it because it is the only way of knowing what goes on in a middle-class family.'

1716 *Tennis*

What is the name of the Australian player, the only player to win the Grand Slam twice, first as an amateur in 1962 and again as a professional in 1969?

1717 *English Law*

What term is used both for the right of the owner of a piece of land to use a public road that is next to the land, and the right of a parent to see a child regularly?

1718 *Medicine*

What is the capacity, in millilitres, of the measuring spoon commonly included with medicines?

1719 *Marine Life*

Dublin Bay and King are two popular types of which edible crustacean of the order *Decapoda*?

1720 *American Literature*

The High Window, *The Lady in the Lake*, *The Big Sleep* and *Farewell My Lovely* are all by which author?

1721 *Ethics*

What ethical principle states that evil methods may be used to produce good effects or results?

1722 *Gymnastics*

What name is given to either of the two handles on a gymnastic horse?

1723 *History*

John Churchill, the victor at the Battle of Blenheim, became the first Duke of where?

1724 *London*

The British Museum, Dickens' House and Birkbeck College are all in which area of London?

1725 *Sporting Events*

What major sporting title is contested annually at the Crucible Theatre in Sheffield?

1726 *Classical Music*

Which English composer wrote several orchestral suites including *By the Sleepy Lagoon*, the theme to *Desert Island Discs* and *The Dam Busters March*?

1727 *Proverbs*

Whose wife, proverbially, must be 'above suspicion'?

1728 *Scotland and Geography*

As in the Kyles of Bute, what is a 'kyle'?

1729 *Quotations*

Who, explaining how she had been able to turn out more than 600 books said, 'When I finish a book I say a prayer and God gives me the plot for the next one.'

1730 *Name Connections*

What name links a Shakespearian king; Edward, the nineteenth-century poet and painter, and a manufacturer of business jet aircraft?

1731 *Roald Dahl*

Charlie Bucket's family is starving because his father has lost his job at a toothpaste factory but the family fortunes change after Willy Wonka holds a contest. What is the book?

1732 *Ancient Rome*

The Roman satirist Juvenal said of the Roman citizenry that they could be pacified by *panem et circenses*. What did that mean?

1733 *The Monarchy and Parliament*

No English monarch has entered the House of Commons since the middle of the seventeenth century. Who was last to do so?

1734 *Politics*

David Waddington 1989–1990, Kenneth Baker 1990–1992, Kenneth Clarke 1992–1993, Michael Howard 1993–1997 and Jack Straw 1997 to the present. Which cabinet position links these men and dates?

1735 *Science*

What trade name is commonly used in this country to refer to many types of poly-methylmetha-crylate?

1736 *Games*

Which two indoor games are governed by the WPBSA?

1737 *Famous Sculptures*

A replica of which famous work by Rodin was bought by the British government and now stands in Victoria Tower Gardens alongside the Houses of Parliament?

1738 *European Football*

Why does the name of the Italian football club AC Milan incorporate the English form of Milan, rather than the Italian, Milano?

1739 *Classic Television*

'If you hadn't nailed it to the perch, it would be pushing up the daisies.' What was John Cleese referring to in a famous Monty Python sketch?

1740 *British Actors*

Which actress was a girlfriend of Ken Barlow's in *Coronation Street*, the athletic Purdey in *The New Avengers*, the time-travelling troubleshooter in *Sapphire and Steel* and the champagne-swilling Patsy in *Absolutely Fabulous*?

1741 *Sport/Business*

Which Australian golfer has a promotion company called the Great White Shark Company?

1742 *Scotland*

Having been immortalized in a romantic boat song, which Scottish island was the site of a local rebellion in the 1990s when citizens refused to pay the large toll fee on the new bridge connecting it to the mainland?

1743 *Cities*

Temple Meads railway station, the M32 motorway and the Royal Portbury Dock all serve which English city?

1744 *Quotations and Music*

Of which German composer did Rossini write that he 'has beautiful moments, but awful quarters of an hour'?

1745 *Cosmetics*

Mrs P.F.E. Albee became the first in 1886, when she began selling perfume door-to-door in New York. The first what?

1746 *Decades*

The Wall Street Crash took place, the British Broadcasting Corporation was established, the Winter Olympics were first staged. The decade?

1747 *Toys and Games*

Which fiendishly complicated six-sided puzzle was the British Association of Toy Retailers Toy of the Year in 1980 and 1981?

1748 *Ancient Literature*

What name, in Aristophenes' comedy *Birds*, is given to the ideal city that is suspended between heaven and earth?

1749 *Board Games*

How many pieces are there on the board at the beginning of a standard game of draughts?

1750 *Television from the 1960s*

Of the seven regular members of which innovative comedy team, first shown in the late 1960s, was Carol Cleveland the only woman?

1751 *The New Testament*

First used in the Bible, as the price of Judas Iscariot's services, what expression has become synonymous with the price of betrayal?

1752 *Films of the 1990s*

In which 1993 comedy did Tom Hanks play Sam Baldwin and Meg Ryan play Annie Reed, the title possibly suggesting a bout of insomnia in northwest USA?

1753 *The Eighteenth Century*

The loss of what, by a Captain Robert Jenkins in 1731, provoked an Anglo–Spanish conflict named after his loss?

1754 *The UK*

Maidstone is the administrative centre for which county?

1755 *British Societies*

The BTS is a society founded in 1950 to create a philosophy of self-control and abstinence from harmful substances. What does BTS stand for?

1756 *Geography*

Canada, Brazil, Morocco and Portugal all have coastlines on which ocean?

1757 *Literature*

Who in a famous cartoon series are the arch enemies of Asterix the Gaul?

1758 *Charles Dickens*

The pickpocket and fence Isaac Solomons, who operated in London in the 1820s, is thought to be the inspiration for which Dickens character?

1759 *Famous Trials*

In 1925, a schoolteacher called John T. Scopes was put on trial in Tennessee for teaching a controversial theory. Which theory?

1760 *Legal Terms*

What name is given to an event which happens independently of human intervention, such as an earthquake or storm, and which no foresight can provide against?

1761 *London Boroughs*

Waterloo Station, Brixton Prison and the National Theatre are all in which London borough?

1762 *Word Connections*

What term or word is used for both an Islamic religious lawyer and plain clothes worn by someone who normally wears a uniform?

1763 *The USA*

What is the significance of the date 20 January, every four years in the United States, even if that date falls on a Sunday?

1764 *Geography*

Somalia, Sri Lanka and Australia all have coastlines on which ocean?

1765 *The New Testament*

'He took water, and washed his hands before the multitude.' Whose symbolic cleansing from his complicity in Jesus's death is the origin of the proverbial expression 'to wash one's hands of the matter'?

1766 *The Bible*

What fate befell a biblical character who defied God's instruction and turned back to look at the fate of the city of Sodom?

1767 *Latin phrases*

What is the meaning of the Latin phrase *infra dig*?

1768 *London*

Which building was originally erected in Kensington in 1862 to be the venue of a second exhibition after the Great Exhibition of 1851, was moved to its present north London site in 1873 and rebuilt two years later following a fire? In 1936 it became the location of the UK's first permanent television channel.

1769 *The UK*

Approximately 168 miles long by 68 miles wide, what is the name of the submerged sandbank 70 miles off the coast of Yorkshire where, in places, the water is only 40 feet deep?

1770 *Horse Racing*

What was the name of the famous grey racehorse that won the King George VI Chase in 1986, 1989 and 1990, the Cheltenham Gold Cup in 1989 and the Irish Grand National in 1990?

1771 *The UK*

Situated on the south bank of the Thames, which famous institution for stray animals opened in 1860?

1772 *Opera*

The operas *Cavalerria Rusticana* and *Pagliacci* are often performed together. By what affectionate nickname is the double-bill known?

1773 *Horse Racing*

After winning both the English and Irish Derbys in 1981, as well as the King George VI and Queen Elizabeth Diamond Stakes, he was retired to stud. Two years later he disappeared and has never been seen since. Which famous horse?

1774 *The UK*

In 1992, the MP for West Bromwich became the first woman to be appointed to which position at Westminster?

1775 *Famous Fictional Characters*

What is the name of the intuitive, sharp-minded and observant spinster who lives in the village of St Mary Mead and who solves her first case in *Murder at the Vicarage*?

1776 *Abbreviations*

Referring to such talents as telepathy and clairvoyance, what do the letters ESP stand for?

1777 *The Church*

What is the name given to a Church of Scotland's Minister's residence?

1778 *Football*

What religious connection is there in the names of the home grounds of Birmingham City, Exeter City and Newcastle United?

1779 *Items of Clothing*

Which item of clothing is aptly known in French as 'le minimum' and in English sounds as though it has musical connotations?

1780 *Foreign Words and Phrases*

Which German word describes the malicious enjoyment of someone else's misfortune?

1781 *Famous Quotations*

Of which film did Irving Thalberg say to Louis B. Mayer: 'Forget it Louis, no Civil War picture ever made a nickel'?

1782 *Awards*

Which profession held its first awards ceremony in 1999, at which 14 winners received a glass statue of Plato and £20,000 for their schools?

1783 *Legendary Beasts*

The Himalayan ape, or abominable snowman. By what Tibetan name is this creature also known?

1784 *Opera*

Which opera by Rossini tells the story of a maid called Ninetta who is condemned to death for stealing silverware but has a last-minute reprieve when the true, feathery culprit is identified?

1785 *History of the USA*

With which notorious affair in America in the 1970s are the journalists Carl Bernstein and Bob Woodward most famously associated?

1786 *Entertainers*

Who is Judy Garland's Oscar-winning daughter?

1787 *British Cities*

Which city grew up around Tiger Bay, a port that thrived in the nineteenth century in the heyday of the coal industry?

1788 *Cars and Muses*

Which word links the Greek muse of history with a famously advertised model of a motor car made by Renault?

1789 *English Societies*

SOS is an organization that fights to preserve and promote England's 40 traditional counties, as opposed to the county council areas created in 1974. What does SOS stand for?

1790 *Sport*

In which decade were the Summer Olympic Games held in Munich and Montreal?

1791 *Trade Names*

The trade name of which variety of bread is taken from the Latin for 'strength of man'?

1792 *Zoology*

From the Latin word for 'hoof', what word describes an animal that has hooves?

1793 *Musicals*

Rusty, a shy little steam engine, after a number of races, triumphs over Greaseball, the flashy diesel locomotive, and gets hitched to his favourite carriage, Pearl. In which Andrew Lloyd Webber musical?

1794 *Prizes*

In terms of the cash prize that goes with it, which is the world's most valuable award in the field of literature?

1795 *Medical Technology*

An electroencephalography, or EEG, is used to detect electrical activity in which part of the body?

1796 *Sport*

In which sport do Group One, Group Two and Group Three events comprise 'the Pattern'?

1797 *Film Actors*

Which Oscar-winning actor has played an insomniac widower in Seattle, a gay lawyer in Philadelphia and an astronaut on an ill-fated Apollo mission to the Moon?

1798 *Rivers*

Which major European river rises in Switzerland and flows through the Netherlands and into the North Sea near Rotterdam?

1799 *The UK*

Taken from the name of a loving elderly couple in an eighteenth century ballad by Henry Woodfall, what name is given to a social club for elderly people, usually run by volunteers who organize parties and outings?

1800 *The UK*

What is the name of the last major engineering work designed by Isambard Kingdom Brunel that was completed in 1864, after his death, and stands across the River Avon in Bristol?

1801 *The UK*

What are Bisham Abbey in Berkshire, Lilleshall in Shropshire and Holme Pierrepont in Nottinghamshire?

1802 *Science*

What optical phenomenon occurs when falling water droplets are illuminated by sunlight behind the observer, and the sunlight is refracted by and reflected within the droplets?

1803 *Magazines and Comics*

Taking its name from a colloquial term for 'a good time' or a party, which popular children's weekly comic first appeared in 1938?

1804 *Government Finances*

What do the initials PSBR stand for?

1805 *Anglo-Saxon Britain*

Which Anglo-Saxon kingdom, the Earldom of which was resurrected in 1999, was the only English kingdom to escape Danish conquest?

1806 *Shakespeare*

The son of Lord Montagu is infatuated with Rosaline. Learning that she is invited to a ball, at the home of a rival family, he goes to the ball in disguise and falls in love with the daughter of his father's chief rival. In which Shakespeare play?

1807 *Costume*

What kind of garment is a 'dhoti'?

1808 *Food and Drink*

A veal cutlet dipped in egg and crumbs, fried in deep fat: by what Austrian name is this dish known?

1809 *Nursery Rhymes*

In the rhyme, 'Goosey Goosey Gander', why was the old man taken by his left leg and thrown down the stairs?

1810 *Underworld Nicknames*

'Scarface' was the nickname of which legendary American gangster?

1811 *History*

What was the name of the vessel on which Charles Darwin set sail on a world voyage in 1831?

1812 *History*

How many of Henry VIII's children succeeded to the throne?

1813 *The Royal Family*

What is the married name of Princess Alexandra?

1814 *Medicine*

What alternative name is given to the disease Tetanus because the severe muscular spasms make it difficult for sufferers to open their mouths?

1815 *Words*

Which word can mean both to split or divide, and to stick or adhere?

1816 *History of Sport*

In which sport in the 1920s and 1930s were Suzanne Lenglen and Helen Wills Moody famous names?

1817 *Religious Law*

What is the more common name of the list of religious and ethical demands, sometimes referred to as the Decalogue?

1818 *Dogs*

What name is given to the group of gun dogs that can be trained to indicate where game lies by standing motionless and aligning their muzzle, body and tail on the game?

1819 *The UK*

What, near Woolwich in south-east London, was completed in 1982 to, amongst other things, keep Londoners from getting too wet?

1820 *Geography*

Which two islands in the Mediterranean, one French, one Italian, are divided by the Strait of Bonifacio?

1821 *Religious Literature*

In which allegorical work by John Bunyan does Christian search for the Celestial City?

1822 *The Winter Olympics*

Which Italian city has won the bid to stage the Winter Olympics of 2006?

1823 *Geography*

What is the name of the geological fault that lies on the boundary between the North American and Eastern Pacific plates of the Earth's crust, and runs for more than 600 miles through California?

1824 *History of Sport*

Who, in 1985, became the first unseeded, the first German and the youngest-ever winner of the Men's Singles title at Wimbledon?

1825 *Word Connections*

What word can mean a ship with two or more masts, with fore-and-aft rigging, or a glass for sherry?

1826 *History*

Whose three husbands, in the sixteenth century, were Francis II of France, Lord Darnley and The Earl of Bothwell?

1827 *The UK*

In slang terms, why is a lower second class university degree sometimes referred to as a 'Desmond'?

1828 *Sport*

The American Steve Scott has done it 139 times, the New Zealander John Walker 129 times and in 1982 14 men did it in one race. Did what?

1829 *Human Physiology*

Which glands secrete tears?

1830 *The UK*

Films passed by the British Board of Film Classification are put into one of six categories. One of these is known as PG. What does PG stand for?

1831 *Musicals*

Persuaded to attend a school dance by his friend Riff, Tony meets and falls in love with Maria, the sister of Bernardo, the leader of a rival gang. In which musical by Leonard Bernstein and Stephen Sondheim?

1832 *The Middle East*

Which peninsula has coastlines on the Gulf of Suez to the west, the Gulf of Aqaba to the east and the Mediterranean Sea to the north?

1833 *Weights and Measures*

Which single imperial unit is equivalent to 1018 kilograms, 2240 pounds or 20 hundredweight?

1834 *Gardening*

Moneymaker is a prolific variety of what?

1835 *Musicals*

Which gothic musical features Brad and Janet, the wholesome all-American couple, Frank'n'furter, a transvestite from Transylvania and his ghoulish henchman, Riff-Raff?

1836 *The USA*

What is the geographical significance in the USA of Mount McKinley in Alaska and Death Valley in California?

1837 *Famous Trademarks*

Which petroleum company adopted a scallop as its trademark in 1904?

1838 *Words*

What is the meaning of the word 'renaissance'?

1839 *Volunteer Work*

In the context of volunteer work what are CSVs or what does CSV stand for?

1840 *Music*

Which note, sixth on the scale of C major, is the note to which members of an orchestra tune their instruments?

1841 *Science*

What is the only substance on Earth that is naturally present in three different forms: liquid, solid and gas?

1842 *Connections*

What word links a type of shoe with a distinctive heel, a type of golf club and a tapering piece of wood?

1843 *Proverbs*

Not strictly true, but according to the proverb what does lightning never do?

1844 *Decades*

In which decade did Cliff Richard have his first record in the UK singles chart?

1845 *Horse Racing*

The five English classics are open to horses of what age?

1846 *Children's Literature*

Who wrote the verse collections *When We Were Very Young* and *Now We Are Six*, and the story 'The House at Pooh Corner'?

1847 *Art and Painting*

The Florentine noblewoman, Lisa del Goicondo, was, in the sixteenth century, the subject of which famous painting, now in the Louvre in Paris?

1848 *Music*

A string quartet traditionally comprises two violins and which two other instruments?

1849 *Famous Marriages*

Who is the comedienne Dawn French married to?

1850 *Photography*

What name is given to the opening that allows light through the lens?

1851 *Geometry*

What name is given to a triangle in which one interior angle is 90 degrees?

1852 *Sports and Games*

In which game, developed by British army officers in India in the 1870s, might you pot, screw or stun the ball in order to clear the table and win the frame?

1853 *The UK*

Darlington, Consett and Bishop Auckland are all in which county?

1854 *Computer Terminology*

What term usually associated with a gesture made when friends meet is used for signals sent between two computers to establish that they are compatible and the data transfer between them is correct?

1855 *International Communication*

Golf, Hotel, India. What comes next?

1856 *Film Quotes*

Where does this come from: 'Toto, I have a feeling we're not in Kansas any more…'?

1857 *French Leaders*

What was the name of the general and statesman who led the Free French during World War Two and later served as President of France?

1858 *Roman Mythology*

Who are these two? Thrown as babies into the Tiber, they were carried to the Palatine where they were suckled by a she-wolf, then raised by a shepherd.

1859 *Crime in the USA*

In which famous incident in the USA, in 1929, were the gangs of Bugs Moran and Al Capone allegedly involved?

1860 *Children's Literature*

Originally called Edward, by what name is A.A. Milne's 'bear of very little brain' better known?

1861 *Scottish Inventors*

Which item of waterproof clothing gets its name from the Scottish inventor who patented the rubberized cloth?

1862 Cartoons

What is the name of the yellow bird who is Snoopy's friend in the cartoon strip?

1863 Law

What is the minimum age you must be to be liable for jury service in the UK?

1864 Geography

Which major river forms the border between Zimbabwe and Zambia?

1865 Sport

Feyenoord, PSV Eindhoven and Ajax are football teams in which European country?

1866 Maths

What name is given to the instrument, generally having the form of a semi-circle, used to construct and measure angles?

1867 Religion and Pop Music

What name links the Italian name for the Virgin Mary and an American megastar?

1868 Education

What is the earliest age at which a pupil can legally leave school in England?

1869 Sport

Which numbers are normally worn by the forwards of a rugby union team?

1870 World War One Poetry

'Anthem for Doomed Youth' and 'Strange Meeting' are both poems by which World War One poet, who died just days before the Armistice?

1871 Films of the 1990s

Who played the roles of Cruella DeVille in 101 Dalmatians, the President's wife in Mars Attacks and Gertrude in Hamlet?

1872 World War Two

What is the significance of the dates 8 May and 15 August 1945?

1873 Geography

In which Irish province is the county of Tipperary?

1874 *Film Music*

The soundtrack of which film, released in 1997, became the fastest-selling and biggest-selling film score ever?

1875 *Words*

What word can mean a strong, sweet, dark red fortified wine, the left-hand side of a ship or a town or place possessing a harbour?

1876 *Famous Nicknames in Russian History*

Ivan IV was the first Tsar of Russia. By what famous sobriquet or nickname has he also become known?

1877 *Sport*

In which sport are there major tournaments called the US Masters and the US PGA?

1878 *English Literature*

What surname was shared by the author of *Tom Brown's Schooldays* and the poet laureate who died in October 1998?

1879 *Botany*

What is the name of the sugary fluid produced by flowers and collected by bees?

1880 *Mathematics*

The prefix 'nano' indicates what fraction?

1881 *The USA*

Of which US state was Bill Clinton elected governor five times before winning the US presidency in 1992?

1882 *Geography*

Cathay is an historical or poetic name for which country?

1883 *Motor Racing*

In motor racing, a yellow flag is hoisted to warn drivers of some danger ahead and not to overtake. What does a red flag signify?

1884 *Connections*

What number connects the Champions of Christendom, the Deadly Sins and the Wonders of the Ancient World?

1885 *EastEnders*

Wendy Richards plays Pauline Fowler. Who plays her son, Mark Fowler, in *EastEnders*?

1886 *Famous People*

Who is this: he joined the Navy in 1770 when just 12 years old, was a captain by the age of 20, lost an eye in 1794, an arm in 1797 and was killed at the height of his greatest victory in 1805?

1887 *The USA*

What, in New York, are Bloomingdales, Saks Fifth Avenue and Macy's?

1888 *Sport*

In which sport do players compete in an enclosed courtyard that is 9.75 metres by 6.4 metres, hitting a black rubber ball alternately against the front wall, above the tin?

1889 *The UK*

The names of three British counties begin with the letter L. Name two of the three.

1890 *Biology*

What is the singular form of the word 'bacteria'?

1891 *Monarchy*

Which of Henry VIII's six wives was the first?

1892 *Television*

What term was coined by Jim Henson to describe his creations which were a blend of marionettes and puppets?

1893 *Literature*

Part of the plot of which Oscar Wilde play was inspired by a report in the *Worthing Gazette* of 11 July 1894 that 'a baby in a hamper had been found at King's Cross Station'?

1894 *Medicine*

What name is given to the yellowing of the skin often present in new-born babies and which, later in life, is associated with the disease hepatitis?

1895 *The Sea*

What is a tsunami?

1896 *Words*

'Pram' meaning a baby carriage is a contraction of which word?

1897 *The Calendar*

All Souls' Day, All Saints' Day and St Andrew's Day. All fall in which month of the year?

1898 *The UK*

What name is popularly given to someone born within the sound of the bells of St Mary-le-Bow church in the City of London?

1899 *Nursery Rhymes*

Which military commander in a nursery rhyme marched his army up and down a hill?

1900 *History*

For his part in which sixteenth-century adventure against England is the Spanish Duke of Medina Sidonia now best remembered?

1901 *Geography*

Portugal shares a land border with only one other country. Which one?

1902 *European Literature*

In which Alexandre Dumas novel does the young D'Artagnan arrive in Paris from Gascony and become involved in three duels with men later to become his friends and colleagues?

1903 *Quotations*

Who, arriving in New York at the age of 18, announced at the New York Custom House: 'I have nothing to declare except my genius'?

1904 *Towns*

Which spa town, at the foot of the Cotswolds, was the birthplace of the composer Gustav Holst, has a famous public girls' school and a racecourse where the Gold Cup is held annually?

1905 *Fictional Characters*

The name of which fictional character, created by the humorist James Thurber, is now an epithet for anyone who takes refuge from reality in elaborate and heroic fantasies?

1906 *Saints*

What is the name of the tenth-century Duke of Bohemia, who is the patron saint of the Czech Republic, and the 'good king' in a popular carol?

1907 *Food and Drink*

What dish, made from chopped lungs, heart and liver mixed with oatmeal, and boiled in a sheep's stomach, is considered a national dish of Scotland?

1908 *History of the USA*

Who was shot at Ford's Theatre in Washington in 1865, while watching a play called *Our American Cousin*?

1909 *Name Connections*

What name links the Greek goddess of the rainbow, a genus of approximately 300 species of flowering plant and the coloured part of the human eye?

1910 *The UK*

Which city in the north of England is an archiepiscopal seat of the Church of England?

1911 *Films of the 1990s*

Who played Louis XIV, and his twin brother, in the 1998 release *The Man in the Iron Mask*?

1912 *Medicine*

Noctambulation and somnambulism are medical terms for what?

1913 *Motoring*

Which unpopular devices were first installed in the UK in July 1958 outside the American Embassy in Grosvenor Square in London – quite appropriately since they were an American invention?

1914 *London*

Which area of London was named Battlebridge until the 1830s when it was then named after a statue of George IV that stood at a crossroads there?

1915 *Politics*

What was the name of the military treaty, signed between the USSR and seven East European countries in 1955 and disbanded in 1991?

1916 *Ancient History*

Which was the most important of the Greek oracles?

1917 *The UK*

In which county are Alnwick Castle, Bamburgh Castle and Chillingham Castle?

1918 *The UK*

What is the Calf of Man?

1919 *Card Games*

What is the usual term for the extra hand that may be dealt to an imaginary player in some card games?

1920 *Decades*

In which decade was oil discovered in the North Sea, did Francis Chichester sail single-handed round the world and the QE2 make her maiden crossing of the Atlantic?

1921 *History*

On which great political charter, signed in the eighteenth century, does the signature of John Hancock appear?

1922 *Literature*

Who could be described as Charles Kingsley's aquatic infants?

1923 *The Royal Family*

Which of the Queen's four children is lowest in the line of succession?

1924 *History of Film*

Which film company was famous for its productions of big musicals, including *Easter Parade, On the Town* and *Singin' in the Rain*?

1925 *The Bible*

Why is the Book of Numbers so called?

1926 *Decades in Sport*

In which decade did the cricketer Denis Compton score a record 3816 runs in one county season, the Dutch athlete Fanny Blankers-Koen win four gold medals at the London Olympics and Bruce Woodcock become the British Heavyweight Boxing champion?

1927 *Human Anatomy*

What is the name of the small muscular sac attached to the underside of the liver and connected to the small intestine by the bile duct?

1928 *Famous Quotations*

This one from Benjamin Franklin: 'We must indeed all hang together, or most assuredly, we shall all…' what?

1929 *Political History*

Which series of laws, passed in the UK in the early nineteenth century, prohibited or discouraged the importation of grain?

1930 *Heraldry*

In heraldry the term 'cowardly' is used to describe an animal in what position?

1931 *The House of Commons*

What name is given to the Members of Parliament who count the votes during a division at the House of Commons?

1932 *Food and Drink*

A nectarine is a smooth-skinned variety of which fruit?

1933 *The USA*

Covering only 1000 square miles, which is the smallest state in the USA?

1934 *The British Monarchy*

Who were the first three reigning monarchs of the seventeenth century?

1935 *The Bible*

What was the name of the rebel and murderer who was released to the Jews by Pontius Pilate in preference to Jesus?

1936 *Famous Lines*

Who spoke these words in a famous radio broadcast in the United States in 1938: 'Ladies and gentleman, I have a grave announcement to make. Incredible as it may seem, strange beings who landed in New Jersey tonight are the vanguard of an invading army from Mars…'?

1937 *The USA*

Cheyenne is the capital of which state?

1938 *Commonwealth*

The British North American Act of 1867 established which Dominion?

1939 *The Bible*

What is the name of the village that was the site of Jesus' first miracle?

1940 *Australia*

Captain Cook first called it Stingray Harbour. How is it now known?

1941 *Geography*

What is the purpose of seeding clouds with carbon dioxide or silver iodide?

1942 *The Eighteenth Century*

Which club, notorious for its debauchery and performance of black masses, was founded by Sir Francis Dashwood during the 1740s?

1943 *The USA*

Sacramento is the capital of which state?

1944 *Jury Service*

During which five-year period of life does an adult who is summoned for jury service have the right to decline?

1945 *Pastimes*

Which card game, which originated in the seventeenth century, is played two, three or four players with 52 cards and a pegboard for scoring?

1946 *Mathematics*

What Latin word meaning a 'square board' is used for the calculating device, still popular in the East, that consists of beads on a wire and wood frame?

1947 *History of the USA*

The population of California grew from some 15,000 in early 1848, to over 100,000 the following year. What event caused this increase?

1948 *Art*

In which Russian city is the famous Hermitage Museum?

1949 *Aviation*

What term is used to refer to the specific category of aircraft the maximum take-off weight of which must not exceed 390 kilograms?

1950 *Pastimes*

What is the proper name for the hobby of stamp-collecting?

1951 *The UK*

Two English counties border on Scotland. Which two?

1952 *Botany*

Aesculus hippocastanum is the Latin name of which large spreading deciduous tree?

1953 *Chess*

Which chessman is both a minor piece and a line piece, moves on diagonals of one colour only, and can neither occupy nor attack the 32 squares of the opposite colour?

1954 *Famous Families*

Herbert was a twentieth-century British prime minister, his son Anthony was a famous film director. What was their family name?

1955 *Word Connections*

What word can be used for either a lilting Irish accent or a strong outdoor shoe, usually decorated with ornamental perforated bands?

1956 *Famous Couples*

The writer and historian Antonia Fraser has a famous husband. Who is he?

1957 *Quotations*

Which former Conservative MP, now a broadcaster and football pundit, and himself a lawyer, once said on *Question Time* on BBC1, 'Lawyers are like rhinoceroses: thick-skinned, short-sighted and always ready to charge'?

1958 *Mathematics*

What is half of three-quarters?

1959 *Theatre*

The Cherry Orchard, *The Seagull* and *The Three Sisters* are plays by which Russian dramatist?

1960 *Law and Order*

What name is given to the vigilance schemes, run by ordinary citizens in order to help the police combat crime in local areas?

1961 *Costume*

Fourchettes and quirks are parts of which item of clothing?

1962 *Cities*

Ormond Quay, Merrion Square and the Parnell Monument are landmarks in which European city?

1963 *Geography*

Which Middle Eastern country has coastlines on the Red Sea and the Persian Gulf?

1964 *Landmarks*

What is the entrance to the Tower of London from the River Thames known as?

1965 *Mathematics*

What is the square root of 169?

1966 *Politics*

Which member of the Cabinet was formerly a steward on the Cunard line?

1967 *Geography*

On which river is the Aswan High Dam?

1968 *Saints' Days*

15 July is the feast day of which saint, once the Bishop of Winchester and trusted advisor to the West Saxon King Ethelwulf?

1969 *History*

What links the names through history of Gavril Princip in 1914, Mathuram Godse in 1948 and Sirhan Bishara Sirhan in 1968?

1970 *Famous Sculptures*

In which city is there a pair of large metal sculptures called the Liver Birds on the Royal Liver building, overlooking the harbour?

1971 *People*

In which field are Sir Basil Blackwell, Sir Stanley Unwin and Sir Victor Gollancz famous names?

1972 *Medicine*

Which constituent of the human body is affected by the hereditary disorder thalassaemia?

1973 *Music*

Which series of 14 pieces of music by Edward Elgar has the dedication 'To my friends pictured within'?

1974 *Parliament*

What term denotes the most severe instruction to Members of Parliament that they must vote in a division of the House, supporting their party?

1975 *Geography*

What nationality is a Helvetian?

1976 *London*

What, in London, is known as 'The Old Lady of Threadneedle Street'?

1977 *Navigation*

What is the name given to the qualified coastal navigator taken on board ship for the purpose of conducting her into and out of port?

1978 *Astronomy*

Which institution is known by the initials RGO?

1979 *Literature*

The Monmouth Rebellion and the assizes of Judge Jeffreys form part of the background to which romantic novel by R.D. Blackmore?

1980 *Charles Dickens*

In a Dickens novel, Mr Brownlow adopts a son of Agnes Fleming. What is the name of the boy?

1981 *The USA*

What's the name of the famous highway running 30 miles from downtown Los Angeles to the Pacific Ocean, which is also the title of an Andrew Lloyd Webber musical?

1982 *Art and Films*

Which nineteenth-century French artist was the subject of the 1950s film *Moulin Rouge*?

1983 *Quotations*

W.C. Fields said: 'Never give a sucker...' what?

1984 *Theatre*

What term is given to a monologue representing a character's thoughts?

1985 *Counties*

The Roseland Peninsula, the Penwith Peninsula and the Lizard Peninsula are all in which county?

1986 *Geography*

What is the name of the ancient paved highway that extended from Rome via Capua to the Adriatic?

1987 *The World of Comedy*

Once part of a famous comedy duo, his real name was Arthur Stanley Jefferson. How was he famously known?

1988 *Literature*

How is the daughter of Professor Archimedes Q. Porter of Baltimore, USA, better known in a series of novels by Edgar Rice Burroughs?

1989 *History of the Oscars*

Who, in 1938, was awarded an honorary Oscar consisting of one proper statue and a collection of miniature statuettes in recognition of a significant screen innovation?

1990 *Literature*

Ring of Bright Water, published in 1960: whose account of his life in a cottage on the west coast of Scotland with two semi-wild otters inspired the story?

1991 *Darts*

What is the highest score a player can make in darts, by hitting a treble?

1992 *Politics*

Who led the Labour Party to defeat in the general elections of 1987 and 1992?

1993 *Word Connections*

What word can mean a chamber for storing grain, an airtight pit for storing green fodder or an underground chamber housing a guided missile?

1994 *Popular Music*

Who was advised by Noël Coward, in a song, not to encourage her offspring to enter the acting profession?

1995 *Environment*

What word can mean to remove the branches from the main trunk of a tree, or to remove the horns from cattle?

1996 *Art*

A Venetian painter, born in 1697, famous for his views of Venice and of London, where he stayed in the mid-eighteenth century: what is his name?

1997 *Horse Racing*

In Royal Ascot week, what is the Thursday called?

1998 *Twentieth-century Novels*

An odiously rich American tycoon is murdered in his sleeping compartment on a transcontinental train. He has been stabbed to death, and each of the occupants of the coach are found to have a motive for his murder: in which famous detective novel?

1999 *Telling the Time*

Where, or on what, might you find a gnomon?

2000 *Mathematics*

What proper fraction is represented as a decimal as 0.333 recurring?

ROUND ONE
Answers

1 Fungus

2 Northern Alaska

3 ME (Myalgic Encephalomyelitis)

4 Cairo

5 William Blake

6 Portsmouth

7 David, Jonathan

8 Harp

9 Glyndebourne Opera House

10 Rugby League

11 *The Silence of the Lambs*

12 *Third Rock from the Sun*

13 Geometry

14 'Kingdom'

15 Peter Shaffer

16 Mauritius

17 *Hansard*

18 The Milky Way

19 Prorata

20 Compact Disc Read Only Memory

21 Kevin Costner

22 He cured a blind man

23 Honeysuckle

24 Alfred Hitchcock

25 *A Clockwork Orange*

26 Major Barbara

27 The Royal Company of Archers

28 Glasgow, Liverpool, Newcastle-upon-Tyne

29 The Bronx

30 Spain

31 'For Valour'

32 *Brigadoon*

33 The story of Noah and the Flood

34 Roland Garros

35 'Rule Britannia'

36 Seven

37 Tarzan

38 The clockwork radio

39 A cheval glass or horse-
dressing glass

40 Fiat

41 Emerald

42 Blood

43 Devon

44 The Alamo

45 The Atlantic Charter

46 Cells

47 1960s

48 Frequently asked
questions

49 Salman Rushdie

50 An Emmy

51 *Who's Afraid of Virginia
Woolf?*

52 Bermuda

53 *Coppelia*

54 Hecate

55 Australian Capital
Territory

56 Shintoor Shintoism

57 The Royal Free

58 A women's university

59 Spring

60 The Pennine Way

61 Maine

62 Chlorophyll

63 Frankie Vaughan

64 Two: The Derby, The Oaks

65 Perfect pitch, absolute
pitch

66 Swansea

67 Pasteurization

68 Richard I

69 The Florida Keys

70 Pluto

71 Close seasons

72 Royal Ascot

73 Babel

74 Sheffield

75 Duchy Originals

76 Boris Pasternak

77 Sixteenth

78 Dante Alighieri

79 Kelpie

80 Charles I was executed

81 Austria, Finland, Sweden

82 Disc Operating System

83 ENT (ear, nose, throat)

84 The Bill of Rights

85 Princess Margaret

86 Greece

87 *Victor ludorum*

88 Rugby League

89 Cobalt

90 Lundy

91 Triple jump

92 Midas

93 Ruth, Esther

94 Cuba

95 Weatherfield

96 Samurai

97 Cello

98 Maundy Thursday

99 Lily Savage

100 Hampshire

101 Retail Price Index

102 Nairobi

103 Celine Dion

104 21

105 Physicians

106 The Brontës

107 *Romeo and Juliet*

108 Bones

109 Sylvia Plath

110 50 metres

111 Byte

112 La Scala

113 C'est la vie

114 Mozart

115 Brother

116 *Red Dwarf*

117 Horse and chariot racing

118 Venus

119 The Indian Ocean

120 Television channels

121 1 March

122 Nashville

123 Daphne du Maurier

124 University of Strathclyde, Glasgow Caledonian University

125 Law, medicine

126 Handwriting

127 New England

128 Oliver Cromwell

129 The Isle of Man

130 Assorted snacks served with drinks

131 Switzerland

132 *Le Monde*

133 '... Benetton'

134 South Africa

135 Bristol

136 Peter Phillips

137 Poseidon

138 The Netherlands

139 The Nile

140 Richard Wagner

141 It is without water

142 Formula 1 motor racing (Grand Prix)

143 America On Line

144 Dead Sea Scrolls

145 *James and the Giant Peach*

146 The Artful Dodger

147 Ornithology

148 Australia

149 Elizabeth I

150 Shirley Eaton

151 J.S. Bach

152 Edinburgh Castle

153 Sinking of the *Lusitania*

154 *The Invisible Man*

155 Brazil

156 Alexander the Great

157 France

158 1920s

159 Fanny Blankers-Koen

160 Malta

161 The moon

162 George VI

163 24

164 Order of Companions of Honour

165 The Nemean Lion

166 The Queen of Sheba

167 Africa

168 Site of Special Scientific Interest

169 The Duke of Kent

170 Shannon (Republic of Ireland)

171 Harare

172 Russia

173 Cross-examination

174 Portsmouth, Southampton

175 Jerusalem

176 Barbara Euphan Todd

177 Trafalgar

178 James Callaghan

179 Foreign and Commonwealth Office

180 Gatwick

181 Acetic

182 New Zealand

183 Dog days

184 Front of house

185 Salisbury

186 Stephen, John, Anne, Victoria

187 Laurence

188 Aeolian harp

189 Clement Attlee

190 Member of the House of Representatives

191 Samuel Langhorne Clemens

192 Ancient lights

193 The Hermitage

194 Glasgow

195 Rio de Janeiro

196 Kent

197 Henry VIII

198 Julian Barnes

199 Nuclear reactors

200 The father of King Arthur

201 Other things being equal

202 Orange

203 *War and Peace*

204 The Master of the Rolls

205 Othello

206 A private box

207 Manchester

208 Fishing

209 Ice hockey

210 Tierra del Fuego

211 Herbert Asquith, David Lloyd George

212 X-rays

213 The Sons of Glendower

214 Louise Brown

215 Simplon Pass

216 *Ruddigore*

217 The Humber

218 Heathcliff

219 *Buddy*

220 Covered with something resembling wool

221 *Little Voice*

222 The Korean War

223 France

224 Anna Friel

225 The Book of Psalms

226 Front

227 Lincolnshire

228 Diwali

229 Collarbone

230 Astronautics

231 Amber

232 Yachting

233 Henry VII

234 Seventeenth

235 Leeds and Bradford

236 Dr Geoffrey Fisher

237 Greece

238 Cruiserweight

239 Fermat's Last Theorem

240 Sanskrit

241 Deuteronomy

242 Gilbert and Sullivan

243 Eddie Murphy

244 The Wash

245 Northumberland

246 The Synoptic Gospels

247 Oedipus

248 Kenya

249 Symphonies

250 They scored for both teams

251 *Exchange and Mart*

252 David

253 Germ warfare

254 Prince Philip

255 In the same place

256 St Mark's Square

257 Adrian Mole

258 Edward VII

259 They observe Saturday rather than Sunday

260 Time zones

261 The London Stock Exchange

262 Sandhurst

263 The Amazons

264 The Nikkei Index

265 Stonehenge

266 Brunel

267 Sir Walter Scott

268 Waterloo

269 Kensington Gardens

270 The BBC

271 Durham

272 Tropic of Cancer

273 Boudicca (or Boadicea)

274 Bat

275 21

276 St James's Palace

277 Glasgow

278 Vodka

279 St Petersburg

280 Oxford

281 Simon

282 Mah Jongg

283 Virginia

284 The Bayeux Tapestry

285 Damien Hirst

286 Poet Laureate

287 Hampshire

288 The Beatles

289 Via Dolorosa

290 The Green Party

291 Madame Tussaud's

292 Advocates

293 Daedalus

294 An arbitrator

295 The Halifax

296 The Great Fire

297 The Commonwealth of Australia

298 *Four Weddings and a Funeral*

299 Hadrian's Wall

300 *Titanic*

301 Northamptonshire

302 Helen of Troy's

303 The Basques

304 Oddjob

305 1 horsepower

306 Liverpool

307 Stamps

308 The Bass Strait

309 Macbeth

310 Spock

311 A goat

312 Canada

313 QC

314 They are all shopping centres

315 Swedish

316 Isaac

317 70

318 Culture, Media and Sport

319 Bangladesh

320 Formula One motor racing

321 Lancaster, York

322 The Autumn Double

323 The Lord Mayor

324 The Open University

325 Rex or Regina

326 Berlin

327 Robert Louis Stevenson

328 The Wombles

329 Ready Steady Cook

330 Sixteenth, seventeenth

331 Mowgli

332 Space stations

333 Polish

334 Bum bag

335 Hewlett Packard

336 Pakistan

337 Easter Island

338 Birmingham

339 Deciduous

340 Compact Video Disk

341 Belgium

342 *Hamlet*

343 Doctor Dolittle

344 The Getty Museum

345 *The Mousetrap*

346 Hay fever

347 Cleopatra

348 Molars

349 The stomach

350 China

351 Orange

352 The Taj Mahal

353 The yen

354 Uganda

355 Dormouse

356 Endangered or threatened species

357 He or she goes to jail

358 *New Musical Express*

359 Central Nervous System

360 Coventry

361 Television

362 Galileo Galilei

363 Her pocket

364 Essex

365 Chicken and leeks

366 Gravity

367 Advent

368 Train ticket

369 Jerusalem

370 Amnesty International

371 Williams

372 Pennsylvania

373 Las Vegas

374 Thor

375 The USA

376 *20,000 Leagues Under the Sea*

377 Theseus

378 *Tom Brown's Schooldays*

379 *Star Wars*

380 *The Simpsons*

381 Ferry services

382 Harry Enfield

383 Sicily

384 The Zambezi

385 Monaco

386 1971

387 15 millilitres

388 Here lies

389 The Republic of Ireland

390 Senegal

391 A silk purse

392 The East River

393 York

394 *1984*

395 Exodus

396 Hinduism

397 Gemini

398 Arabic

399 Marshalsea

400 Pakistan

401 Mahler

402 Sikhism

403 Trinidad and Tobago

404 Italy

405 George Eliot

406 A brain

407 George I

408 *Emma*

409 Stroke

410 Theatre directors

411 Longchamp

412 The Calcutta Cup

413 The Oaks

414 Buckinghamshire

415 Risk

416 Frankie Dettori

417 Pundit

418 The University Boat Race

419 Royal Flying Doctor Service

420 Atomic number

421 Catalan

422 Sir Thomas More

423 The Indian Ocean

424 Eddie Stobart

425 1911

426 Yellow

427 *Cymbeline*

428 Direct Memory Access

429 Richmond-upon-Thames

430 Six

431 John Bunyan

432 The Lake District
National Park

433 London Commodity
Exchange

434 *The French Lieutenant's
Woman*

435 Motor racing

436 Building societies

437 '... invention'

438 The Security Council

439 Diana

440 Sweden

441 Barnaby Rudge

442 The Bible

443 The burning of the ballot
papers

444 Rabat

445 '... omnipotent'

446 Art galleries

447 Constantine the Great

448 MENCAP

449 Save the Children Fund

450 Commonwealth Games

15 to 1

ROUND TWO
Answers

451 Spinach

452 The blood (it is a clotting agent, deficiency causes haemophilia)

453 *The Merry Wives of Windsor*

454 Romans (The Epistle of Paul the Apostle to the Romans)

455 Cars

456 The Coronation service

457 Switzerland, Italy

458 Nottinghamshire

459 Alexandra

460 Chinese

461 Tottenham Hotspur

462 Tutankhamen

463 Africa (Morocco, Algeria, Tunisia, Libya and Egypt)

464 Onshore oil fields

465 St Aidan

466 The Press Complaints Commission

467 Single Transferable Vote

468 Mrs Be-done-by-as-you-did

469 England, Scotland

470 Cio-cio-san

471 The Graces (or Charities, or Gratiae)

472 Break-even point

473 Belvedere

474 General Issue (stamped on equipment) or Government Issue (modern meaning)

475 Richard I (Richard the Lionheart)

476 Oxygen

477 *Brief Encounter*

478 The Armada

479 Man walking on the moon

480 Foreign Secretary

481 Pretoria

482 Paella

483 The Sorceror

484 An atmosphere

485 Five (won four, lost one)

486 Organization of African Unity

487 A surface-to-air missile

488 Hereward the Wake

489 Katmandu

490 *Sense and Sensibility*

491 May

492 Corroborative evidence

493 Chief Secretary to the Treasury

494 Dr Doolittle

495 Burmese

496 Mohs scale

497 Glamis Castle

498 Vincent van Gogh

499 Fourth day

500 Error in dating

501 *A Tale of Two Cities*

502 Circuits

503 If God wills/God willing

504 April

505 Pina colada

506 *West Side Story*

507 Boxing

508 Bouncers

509 The care and resettlement of offenders and prevention of crime

510 Cousin (first cousin)

511 Wiltshire

512 Athos, Porthos, Aramis

513 As though speaking

514 Mycroft

515 Tutsi, Hutu

516 Glass

517 Green, blue, red

518 Simple interest

519 Boxing

520 Copper, zinc

521 The only British-born undisputed heavyweight boxing world champion (1897)

522 *The Catcher in the Rye*

523 Airports

524 *The Sound of Music*

525 Docklands Light Railway

526 From day to day

527 Edward VIII

528 Howe

529 The Vietnam War

530 Benjamin Disraeli

531 Secret Intelligence Service

532 The ant

533 Matthew Parker

534 Certificate of Airworthiness

535 Lord Mountbatten

536 René Magritte

537 Sir Henry Rider Haggard

538 The eighteenth

539 Osmosis

540 *A Streetcar Named Desire*

541 Crippen

542 Temporary or improvised

543 Prairie oyster

544 *The Tailor of Gloucester*

545 Fire engine

546 Frans Hals

547 Andrew Bonnar Law

548 Tea

549 Hungary

550 William Burroughs

551 The Duke of Argyll

552 The Foxes

553 Denier

554 Monmouth's rebellion

555 Passion flower or passiflora

556 Jupiter

557 (Arterial) blood pressure

558 Sumo wrestling

559 A

560 G-force

561 Corpus Christi

562 She stabs herself with Romeo's dagger

563 Anniversary of the Queen's wedding to the Duke of Edinburgh

564 Leicestershire

565 Guilty mind (meaning that you intended to carry out a crime knowing it was wrong)

566 Carp

567 Mr Pickwick

568 Plymouth (Sutton division)

569 Roman Catholics

570 The Royal Festival Hall

571 Sophia Loren

572 Cambridgeshire

573 Bunbury

574 Vintage

575 Ramsay MacDonald

576 Antony and Cleopatra

577 Sound

578 War

579 Maryland

580 Robert Browning

581 Vivaldi

582 *Gentlemen Prefer Blondes*

583 The big toe

584 The Rye House Plot

585 *Danse Macabre*

586 The Clerk of the House

587 Grace and Favour

588 Apothecary

589 The Sparrow

590 Cubism

591 *Jane Eyre*

592 *The Sunday Times*

593 House of York

594 Austen Chamberlain

595 1920s

596 Kendo

597 Sally Gunnell

598 Noël Coward

599 1 inch

600 Medicine

601 *Das Kapital*

602 Discovery of the last three planets

603 The Act of Union

604 Mark McCormack

605 Beethoven's

606 Liver

607 Metronome

608 Port Sunlight

609 Fred Astaire

610 The Maginot Line

611 The Open University

612 Ireland

613 Public Record Office

614 Fianna Fail

615 Mike Leigh

616 Chicken

617 Force majeure

618 Internet Service Provider

619 One of them has a small black dot on it (spot white)

620 Mark Antony

621 Pulse

622 Catalyst

623 Dorset, Wiltshire, West Sussex, Surrey, Berkshire

624 James I of England (or James VI of Scotland)

625 Russia

626 110 metre hurdles

627 Work or energy

628 Many (or much)

629 Product

630 Princess Anne (the Princess Royal)

631 Hydrogen

632 Alice

633 Inflation

634 Fish

635 12

636 *Nil desperandum*

637 Sting

638 Coniferous

639 Volvo

640 Virgil

641 Atheist

642 Tiger Woods

643 Mansion House

644 1

645 The Salvation Army

646 Iberia

647 Maiden over

648 *The Likely Lads*

649 *The Jungle Book*

650 The hand

651 Anagram

652 Potassium

653 Manchester

654 Horse racing

655 The heptathlon

656 The opening of the tomb of Tutankhamen

657 The Star-Spangled Banner (US national anthem)

658 Eleventh and twelfth

659 Natural

660 The Crimean War

661 Home Office

662 Celsius

663 Nom de plume

664 The Atlantic Ocean

665 Cricket

666 A mountain range

667 Windows

668 Six runs scored

669 Filament

670 Swans

671 Gazpacho

672 Salzburg

673 Robbie Coltrane

674 By telling him 1001 tales

675 Bathsheba

676 The Temple of Artemis

677 Host talk shows

678 *Absolutely Fabulous*

679 *Oliver!*

680 Blackcurrant

681 Church minister

682 Neolithic

683 BASIC

684 *Swan Lake*

685 Canada

686 Peace

687 Norfolk and Essex

688 Femur

689 Mercury

690 The South Sea Bubble

691 He committed suicide

692 Troy

693 Passover (Pesach)

694 The Sydney Opera House

695 River Severn

696 A chamber orchestra

697 *Silas Marner*

698 India

699 John Brown

700 Logic

701 The Holy Grail

702 Arabic

703 *Les Miserables*

704 John the Baptist

705 Luxembourg

706 Momentum

707 Blue whale

708 Joseph Lister

709 *Oklahoma!*

710 Children's garden

711 A knight

712 Sailing

713 Become gradually softer

714 Treated animal skins

715 Pacemaker

716 Great Ormond Street

717 The Little Mermaid

718 La Manche

719 Banquo

720 The Red Sea

721 Land's End, John O'Groats

722 Orange, lemon

723 Denmark

724 The Lions

725 Hemlock

726 Acceleration

727 Los Angeles

728 Ulster

729 Rupert Brooke

730 Apple

731 Amphibia

732 Virus

733 Bucharest

734 Jealousy

735 *My Fair Lady*

736 Hippolyta

737 ... *Venus*

738 Birmingham

739 Aberdeen

740 Roger

741 B*witched

742 Putting off doing something

743 Rorke's Drift

744 Council for the Protection of Rural England

745 Subjudice

746 The Norman Conquests

747 Emmeline Pankhurst

748 Derby

749 A Cardinal

750 Accent marks above or below words or letters such as cedillas, tildes and circumflexes

751 20 km, 50 km

752 The Queen's Proctor

753 Because it stands on Mons Vaticanus, one of the hills of Rome

754 Mike Hawthorn

755 A wreath of ivy

756 7 is ten times stronger than 6

757 Tumbril or tumbrel

758 *Carry On* films

759 *Doctor Who*

760 1978

761 £5000

762 Umberto Eco

763 The unicorn

764 Peter Blake

765 Surrey

766 *The Tempest*

767 Brass rubbing

768 Genesis

769 10

770 Deacon

771 Town walls

772 Birmingham

773 John Donne

774 That it is the first or brightest star in the constellation

775 South America and Antarctica

776 Dénouement

777 Hit wicket, handled ball, hit ball twice, obstructed the field, timed out

778 The World Service

779 Great-great-granddaughter

780 Anthony van Dyke

781 Bertolt Brecht

782 Methuselah

783 *The Aeneid*

784 George II

785 Martin Pipe

786 Mumps

787 Radar (Radio Detection and Ranging)

788 Penguin Books

789 Alexandra Palace

790 Kieran Prendiville

791 Prince Edward

792 Lake Geneva

793 Microfiche

794 Christchurch

795 The action of focusing the eye

796 Quebec

797 Tuna

798 Hagiography (hagiology)

799 Clink

800 The Brothers Karamazov

801 October

802 Headache

803 Uruguay

804 The Good Samaritan

805 The palms of the hands or the soles of the feet

806 The Labour Party

807 Point in orbit when furthest from the sun

808 The Comet

809 Retro-rockets

810 Go, Just Visiting (Jail); Free Parking; Go to Jail

811 Arrowroot

812 Porphyria

813 Alexander the Great

814 Grace Kelly

815 The Andes

816 Delphinium

817 Police and Criminal Evidence Act

818 Sulphuric acid

819 Mickey Mouse

820 A sumo wrestling tournament

821 ... *Robinson Crusoe*

822 Mercury

823 *The African Queen*

824 Every 500 years

825 Chester

826 January

827 Uranus

828 August

829 Henry Moore

830 John Thaw

831 Huddersfield

832 *The Comedy of Errors*

833 Watling Street

834 Marmalade

835 Cesarewitch

836 Venezuela

837 Sir Joshua Reynolds

838 Amalgam

839 Little Tommy Tucker

840 John Philip Sousa

841 Fibre optics

842 The Caribbean

853 Kublai Khan

844 Thomas Telford

845 Anchor

846 Biltong

847 The Sergeant at Arms

848 Yom Kippur (Day of Atonement)

849 Wardour Street

850 Marina

851 The Ligurian Sea

852 They are flightless because they have a keel-less breastbone

853 Israel

854 *The Tenant of Wildfell Hall*

855 Vienna

856 Dorothy Parker

857 Pound

858 *Sweeney Todd*

859 Death

860 Oil press

861 Lieutenant Colonel

862 Archduke Franz Ferdinand

863 Plimsoll line

864 Tempura

865 Great Universal Stores

866 Estuary English

867 Tralee

868 A mirror

869 Summary offences

870 Frederick Delius

871 Sergei Prokofiev

872 Provence

873 House of Commons

874 '... muckle.'

875 Cluedo

876 Experience

877 Duke of Leinster

878 Social workers

879 A newly coined word

880 Lazio (or Latium)

881 *Little Lord Fauntleroy*

882 Slow down

883 Nitrogen

884 U2

885 Lincolnshire

886 Saxe-Coburg (and) Gotha

887 Semi-quaver

888 Blue plaques

889 *The Caretaker*

890 Edward VIII

891 Snapdragon

892 Lilian Baylis

893 A.E. Housman

894 Drag

895 Harry Truman

896 1 or 11

897 South America

898 Ambridge

899 The *Observer*

900 A tooth

901 It's near the shore of the sea, or side of a lake

902 *East of Eden*

903 Seraphim

904 Someone who commits a contempt of court

905 El Dorado

906 A tide that flows in the same direction the wind blows

907 Lamentations

908 The Foreign and Commonwealth Office

909 Daisy

910 Jobsworth

911 Medusa

912 It was brought down

913 Arkansas

914 *Anna Karenina*

915 *The Misfits*

916 Flying Officer

917 Oxford Symphony

918 *Toad of Toad Hall*

919 Tony Warren

920 The Lady of Shallott

921 Berlin

922 *Blood Brothers*

923 Lincoln

924 Mongolia

925 British

926 1 million

927 Talmud

928 Cassandra

929 Musk

930 *Shakespeare in Love*

931 Brendan Behan

932 A surname

933 Urdu

934 The biathlon

935 William Hartnell

936 '... destruction'

937 Boxing

938 The Serious Fraud Office

939 Forgetfulness of the past

940 'The Battle Hymn of the Republic'

941 George IV

942 *The Rake's Progress*

943 Lightning

944 Bermuda

945 Somerset

946 The Pompidou Centre

947 Cumbria

948 Lobby correspondents

949 Recite the Koran by heart

950 Lord Mayor's Procession and Show

951 River Rhone

952 Turkey

953 British Airways

954 Ally McBeal

955 Lord Protector

956 Devon

957 Derbyshire, Leicestershire, Nottinghamshire

958 Mary, Mary quite contrary

959 The brain

960 Rogation days

961 International Directory Enquiries

962 Lake Victoria

963 Comedy

964 The Royal Academy

965 The *Sunday People*

966 Fast breathing

967 Nick Leeson

968 S4C

969 Don Quixote

970 Arpeggio

971 The *London Gazette*

972 Captain Oates

973 *Brief Encounter*

974 Oxfordshire

975 Dummy

976 Romance

977 The Beatles

978 Catherine the Great

979 *Birds of a Feather*

980 Prosthetic

981 22 November 1963

982 '... make mad'

983 The Battle of the Nile

984 Holistic

985 Pony

986 Eiswein

987 Rotterdam, Zeebrugge

988 *The Merry Wives of Windsor*

989 The Knesset

990 Oxford

991 David Balfour

992 Closed-circuit television

993 March

994 Akela

995 *Round the Horne*

996 Minimum Lending Rate

997 The Annunciation

998 Glencoe

999 Quorn

1000 Current

1001 United Arab Emirates

1002 *Id est*

1003 A truck/lorry driver

1004 Luddites

1005 Agamemnon

1006 Reims

1007 July

1008 Stalin

1009 Equity

1010 Agatha Christie

1011 Elizabeth I

1012 Public Enemy No.1

1013 The Scilly Isles

1014 *The Old Curiosity Shop*

1015 Buckinghamshire

1016 Glaciers

1017 Pomegranates

1018 *Persuasion*

1019 The Giant's Causeway and Causeway Coast

1020 Lancashire

1021 Old Contemptibles

1022 Queen Victoria

1023 At the bottom of the sea or a lake

1024 '... success.'

1025 Baptists

1026 Tug of War

1027 Nissen hut

1028 The Forestry Commission

1029 Medical

1030 'The Soldier's Song'

1031 The press

1032 The Campaign for Real Ale

1033 '... pound foolish'

1034 Garrison Keillor

1035 Iconoclast

1036 Private Member's Bills

1037 Crete

1038 Chromium

1039 Polynesia

1040 Mountains

1041 36

1042 Egypt

1043 Tarot cards

1044 Kenneth Williams

1045 Duchy of Lancaster

1046 '... May to December'

1047 Hamlet

1048 Agriculture

1049 Gymnasium

1050 *Jeeves and Wooster*

1051 Montgolfier

1052 Jack Dempsey

1053 Ayatollah

1054 Simply Red

1055 Hyannisport

1056 Crocodile

1057 Circus

1058 *dinnerladies*

1059 Five

1060 The Who

1061 *Toy Story*

1062 Mexico

1063 The size and shape of the cranium

1064 Pythagoras' theorem

1065 The Beach Boys

1066 Italy, Spain

1067 Pressure (of gases)

1068 *Lohengrin*

1069 William IV

1070 Oswestry

1071 Coins

1072 The Central Criminal Court

1073 The Law Society

1074 The Tote

1075 Black

1076 Not proven

1077 The Queen Mother

1078 The Woolsack

1079 A ship is missing

1080 17

1081 The place where William II was killed

1082 Essex, Kent, East Anglia, Sussex

1083 Liverpool

1084 Cow

1085 Swiss Cottage

1086 Raj

1087 Port Stanley

1088 Pontefract

1089 plc

1090 Upon Westminster Bridge (The City of London)

1091 Old age

1192 *Mrs Doubtfire*

1093 A mosque

1094 Queen Victoria

1095 Marianne

1096 The Grand Union Canal

1197 *My Best Friend's Wedding*

1098 Pandora

1099 George III

1100 Lord's Day Observance Society

1101 It's the town's main church

1102 Israel

1103 World War One

1104 An eagle

1105 He set up the McDonald's chain

1106 Thomas à Becket

1107 An acorn

1108 They are symbols of the Democratic Party and the Republican Party

1109 Red and amber

1110 Solvent

1111 Beer, cider

1112 Orienteering

1113 Mercury

1114 The belief that Bacon wrote Shakespeare's plays

1115 North and south poles

1116 Intensive Care Unit

1117 Who Dares Wins

1118 It is a shore establishment

1119 Sir John Betjamen

1120 30 miles per hour

1121 Stomach

1122 32

1123 Sodom and Gomorrah

1124 Albert Schweitzer

1125 Kiev

1126 Loch Ness

1127 A high-speed train

1128 Arsenal

1129 Buddhism

1130 The Spanish Civil War

1131 *Paradise Lost*

1132 Menu

1133 They are all lighthouses

1134 Oxbridge

1135 Tennis

1136 *Armageddon*

1137 Addams

1138 Roald Amundson

1139 Richard Cromwell

1140 Sulphur

1141 Brother and sister

1142 Basmati

1143 Skylark

1144 Greece

1145 Tunisia

1146 Basketball

1147 Cleopatra

1148 Bookmarking

1149 Kidney stone

1150 Pope

1151 Goal shooter, goal keeper

1152 Gibraltar

1153 The Lighthouse Family

1154 Verona

1155 The American Civil War

1156 The Tour de France

1157 In the coal mines

1158 Argentina

1159 Henry Hudson

1160 Personal Identification Number

1161 Ballistics

1162 Five

1163 Lizard

1164 Core, mantle

1165 Colin Dexter

1166 Turkish

1167 Muscles

1168 Impeachment

1169 Colonel Gaddafi

1170 Congruent

1171 *The Hunchback of Notre Dame*

1172 The yak

1173 State Television and Radio (Radio Telefis Eireann)

1174 The Indian Ocean

1175 Carbon

1176 The tomb of Thomas à Becket

1177 Perseus

1178 David Bowie

1179 Interstate

1180 The Apennines

1181 Galvanized

1182 Military Intelligence

1183 Smorgasbord

1184 22 yards

1185 Coventry

1186 Japan

1187 Vauxhall

1188 Goose

1189 Mexico

1190 Muhammed Ali

1191 Metaphor

1192 An ox-bow lake

1193 The Red Baron

1194 Theatre

1195 Loch Lomond

1196 The worshipping of many gods

1197 Director of Public Prosecutions

1198 Gardening

1199 Tonga

1200 Lady Penelope

1201 Sydney Harbour Bridge

1202 Prince Edward

1203 *William Tell*

1204 Professor Henry Higgins

1205 The Paralympic Games

1206 A ward of court

1207 Sailing

1208 Great Salt Lake

1209 Organic

1210 Graham Taylor

1211 Senate

1212 A sonnet

1213 Sri Lanka

1214 Conduction, convection, radiation

1215 The World Health Organization

1216 Oil

1217 People's Dispensary for Sick Animals

1218 Cardiff

1219 Capriccio

1220 Anne

1221 1979

1222 Reducing a sentence to a lesser one

1223 Throwing someone out of a window

1224 Indonesia

1225 Academy

1226 Caries

1227 Chambré

1228 Higher education

1229 Margaret Thatcher

1230 Butch Cassidy and the Sundance Kid

1231 *King Solomon's Mines*

1232 St Alban

1233 Choral festival

1234 60

1235 Sang-froid

1236 Anglesey

1237 Prudence

1238 Standards in Education

1239 Simplon Pass

1240 The Speaker

1241 I think, therefore I am

1242 Concert piano

1243 Hawaii

1244 *Modern Times*

1245 The pH scale

1246 Percussion

1247 Higher National Diploma

1248 Ezekiel

1249 Eurasia

1250 Optic nerve

1251 A trainspotter

1252 Polo

1253 Minnesota

1254 Birmingham

1255 A triptych

1256 Ophelia

1257 1 square mile

1258 A love letter

1259 Work

1260 First half of the eighteenth century

1261 Friends of the Earth

1262 Bodmin Moor

1263 Emergency Room

1264 Anne Boleyn

1265 Anthony Eden, Harold Macmillan

1266 W.H. Auden

1267 Carl Davies

1268 The Grand National

1269 An eye test

1270 Photography

1271 Vorsprung durch Technik

1272 By immersion in baths fed by the holy spring

1273 David Croft

1274 Judi Dench and Michael Williams

1275 Hydrogen

1276 As fighter aces

1277 Transporting the regalia

1278 Spanish

1279 Muhammad

1280 The American Civil War

1281 Mary

1282 *A Midsummer Night's Dream*

1283 *Cave canem*

1284 Admiralty Arch

1285 Ghana

1286 Davy Jones, Mickey Dolenz, Mike Nesmith, Peter Tork

1287 Fortune favours the brave

1288 Margery Allingham

1289 Carlisle

1290 Brown

1291 Milan

1292 Manchester

1293 Spain

1294 New York

1295 Yoghurt

1296 '... aphrodisiac'

1297 William the Conqueror was crowned

1298 Bobby Shafto

1299 Cecil Day Lewis

1300 Bill Clinton

1301 St George and St Andrew

1302 Maine Road

1303 *Schindler's List*

1304 Switzerland

1305 Tynwald Court

1306 Charles II

1307 Lineal, collateral

1308 Cambridge

1309 Obstetrics

1310 Ring roads

1311 Pharaoh

1312 Denmark

1313 Mary Queen of Scots

1314 Helsinki

1315 *The Times*

1316 The International Court of Justice

1317 Bonnie Parker and Clyde Barrow

1318 Honolulu

1319 Lepta

1320 Arctic Circle

1321 Epiphany

1322 The Aland Islands

1323 Ray Galton and Alan Simpson

1324 Perrier

1325 UNIFEM

1326 '… are soon parted'

1327 Dartmouth

1328 They are at right angles

1329 Trollope

1330 ''Tis folly to be wise'

1331 Tungsten (or Wolfram)

1332 A stroke

1333 The pits

1334 Stevie Smith

1335 Love

1336 The court of the Lord Lyon

1337 M62

1338 The shilling

1339 Amsterdam

1340 Mississippi

1341 Four

1342 Sitwell

1343 Icknield Way

1344 Edvard Grieg

1345 '… tongues'

1346 Gardening

1347 Sheffield

1348 Boat-shaped

1349 Community Chest

1350 Lanolin

1351 Any chessman except a pawn

1352 Magpie

1353 Belfast

1354 A mixture of spices

1355 Cambridge

1356 The Trojan War

1357 Edward VI

1358 Benjamin Franklin

1359 Treasure trove

1360 Dog Rose

1361 Henley Regatta

1362 Facsimile transmission

1363 Roman Catholic

1364 The Brecon Beacons

1365 Vienna

1366 Portia

1367 Norse

1368 The Isles of Scilly

1369 Five

1370 A quarter

1371 Halley's Comet

1372 Work in Progress

1373 The Royal Mile

1374 Ice hockey

1375 Pairing

1376 The Earth's surface

1377 Velvet

1378 Tabasco

1379 '… in midstream'

1380 Filament

1381 Chocolate cake

1382 Sir James Dewar

1383 Winchester

1384 The Royal Marines

1385 Swallowing

1386 Madrid

1387 Deadweight Tonnage

1388 Rutland

1389 A night without sleep

1390 Most Favoured Nation

1391 John Keats

1392 Cinderella

1393 Lead

1394 Piedmont

1395 Cost, insurance, freight

1396 *Charlie's Angels*

1397 Gertrude

1398 Philip II of Spain

1399 Victoria

1400 Viscount

15 to 1

ROUND THREE
Answers

1401 The Duke of Windsor

1402 Jacob's

1403 Suffolk, Essex

1404 Plastic surgery

1405 Penicillin

1406 'The Rime of the Ancient Mariner'

1407 Smallpox

1408 'Rumpelstiltskin'

1409 Prince Albert

1410 Winchester

1411 Wells, Fargo

1412 Virginia Wade

1413 The Faroe Islands

1414 Salt Lake City

1415 The first eight books of the Old Testament

1416 Clarence Birdseye

1417 Statue of Liberty (on base)

1418 Cold calling

1419 Whisky (phonetic alphabet)

1420 Jamaica

1421 Woodworm

1422 Feng Shui

1423 Blue chip

1424 Sodium (from Natrium)

1425 The colours of the spectrum/rainbow

1426 Rin-Tin-Tin

1427 The Grim Reaper

1428 The 1950s

1429 The *Wall Street Journal*

1430 Dennis Potter

1431 Blackpool

1432 You will catch neither

1433 Antipasto/Antipasti

1434 Capability Brown

1435 Meniscus

1436 Andy Capp

1437 The Zulu nation

1438 Sherry

1439 'They can't take that away from me!'

1440 Nocturne

1441 All posthumous awards

1442 Mouse

1443 *A Brief History of Time*

1444 *Little Women*

1445 Infinity

1446 St John's Ambulance

1447 Arundel

1448 Southern, south

1449 *2001: A Space Odyssey*

1450 Cats eyes (reflecting road studs)

1451 1 calorie

1452 James Boswell

1453 Doctor Fu Manchu

1454 Noah

1455 Archimedes'

1456 Algebra

1457 Mime

1458 W.G. Grace

1459 Saxophone

1460 Trident

1461 Angostura Bitters

1462 Devon

1463 Nebuchadnezzar

1464 *The Muppet Show*

1465 Edward the Confessor

1466 Captain

1467 Public executions (Tyburn)

1468 Eastings

1469 Rust

1470 They were also the host nations

1471 *One Flew Over the Cuckoo's Nest*

1472 Kedgeree

1473 *Death in Venice*

1474 The Indian Ocean

1475 The Crown Prosecution Service

1476 Norfolk

1477 On the back burner

1478 Driving in a car/motoring

1479 Indonesia, Malaysia, Brunei

1480 Links

1481 Mockingbird

1482 Mary I

1483 Nineteenth

1484 Jimmy Carter

1485 Legoland

1486 Chemin de fer

1487 Archbishop of York

1488 Watling Street

1489 Pins and needles

1490 Belgian

1491 Harlech

1492 *The Crucible*

1493 The Surprise Symphony

1494 Tunisia

1495 Absolute zero

1496 Brut

1497 TT Motorcycle Races

1498 Horses

1499 *Funny Girl*

1500 Berwick-upon-Tweed

1501 Sebastian Coe

1502 Greta Garbo

1503 Joseph of Arimathea

1504 Roger Moore

1505 Sir David Frost

1506 The Gunfight at the OK Corral

1507 *Camelot*

1508 Twiggy

1509 George Michael

1510 Granny flat

1511 Sir Laurence Olivier

1512 1 mile

1513 The USA entered World Wars One and Two

1514 India

1515 *The Messiah* (part two)

1516 Eclipse

1517 Bombay (Mumbai), Calcutta

1518 In a cave

1519 Monty Python

1520 *The Time Machine*

1521 A hologram

1522 Rocks

1523 Clydesdale

1524 The Strait of Gibraltar

1525 Danish

1526 Delta

1527 Parallelogram

1528 Cyprus, Malta

1529 Steal

1530 *The Adventures of Huckleberry Finn*

1531 Evaporation

1532 Pegasus

1533 Ebenezer Scrooge

1534 The Church of Scotland

1535 Sitar

1536 Cappuccino

1537 *Animal Farm*

1538 Diameter

1539 Alberta

1540 24

1541 The Cheviots

1542 Defender of the Faith

1543 Still life

1544 Egyptian

1545 Hamlet

1546 Karaoke

1547 E

1548 The Queen

1549 Decathlon

1550 Flow chart

1551 A mitre

1552 Camp David

1553 The tomb of the unknown soldier

1554 Au pair

1555 A net

1556 Wisdom tooth

1557 A subpoena

1558 Qantas

1559 A volley

1560 Druids

1561 Jumbo

1562 *The Children of the New Forest*

1563 Equinox

1564 The 'Minute Waltz'

1565 Mardi Gras

1566 Mount Everest

1567 Culture Club

1568 Great Britain

1569 It has no tail

1570 Mick Jagger

1571 Greyhound racing

1572 Queen Mary

1573 Pitcairn Island

1574 Van Morrison

1575 Irn Bru

1576 Martina Navratilova

1577 Cornish Pasty

1578 Tent

1579 Cover note

1580 Carnivores

1581 Olive Oyl

1582 Atmospheric pressure

1583 Camelot

1584 Javelin

1585 Luxembourg

1586 Paediatrician

1587 A cat

1588 Joseph Heller

1589 31

1590 Norway

1591 Oxygen

1592 22/7

1593 Altimeter

1594 The Olivier, The Lyttleton, The Cottesloe

1595 Eighteenth

1596 France

1597 The Sphinx

1598 Between an election in November and a new president taking office in January

1599 The General Election (they were fringe parties)

1600 Narcissus

1601 Incognito

1602 Underground rivers

1603 Green

1604 *From Here to Eternity*

1605 Cain and Abel

1606 A laser beam

1607 The Atlantic Ocean

1608 Ramsay MacDonald

1609 Black hole

1610 A warship powered by three banks of oars

1611 Isadora Duncan

1612 Ophelia

1613 60

1614 Denis Law, Kenny Dalglish

1615 '… a ha'porth of tar'

1616 *The Godfather*

1617 *The Archers*

1618 To aid detection because methane is mainly odourless

1619 Outside broadcast

1620 The 1860s

1621 First human heart transplant

1622 King Lear

1623 *Seven Brides for Seven Brothers*

1624 Norman Stanley Fletcher

1625 Tomb of the unknown soldier

1626 Rangers, Celtic

1627 Coral

1628 Screen actors

1629 '… hitting below it'

1630 It was the first to give votes to women

1631 A ridge of hair down its back that grows against the grain (Rhodesian Ridgeback)

1632 Alton Towers

1633 Anvil

1634 Waugh dynasty

1635 Marsala wine

1636 Sir Peter Scott

1637 Helium

1638 Pakistan

1639 Perrier

1640 Home Office (Department of Home Affairs)

1641 'Throwing the baby out with the bathwater'

1642 1415

1643 William Tell

1644 Tuberculosis

1645 Groups of British artists

1646 Paper Tiger

1647 Barcelona

1648 *Mary Poppins*

1649 Canada

1650 Mrs Beeton

1651 Cells

1652 Orbit

1653 Barbra Streisand

1654 Kon-Tiki

1655 *Paradise Regained*

1656 Manhattan Island

1657 The 'Clock Symphony'

1658 The Caspian Sea

1659 The Bloody Tower

1660 Lungs

1661 George Foreman

1662 Goldfinger

1663 Sense of touch

1664 Bismarck

1665 Great-great-great-grandson

1666 Lord Peter Wimsey

1667 Hydrolysis

1668 '...Who could ask for anything more?'

1669 Martin Luther King

1670 The Orkneys

1671 Cairo

1672 Paso Doble

1673 Lady Caroline Lamb

1674 Bethesda

1675 *La Boheme*

1676 Moral Rearmament

1677 Egypt

1678 A series of letters

1679 Dick Whittington

1680 Noblesse oblige

1681 The United States of America

1682 *Arsenic and Old Lace*

1683 New Hampshire, New York

1684 South Africa

1685 Leech

1686 Culloden Moor

1687 Bar code

1688 Sumatra

1689 Glaciers

1690 Fish

1691 Rice

1692 Hamley's

1693 St Albans

1694 John

1695 Hansel and Gretel

1696 Rupert Brooke

1697 Zaire

1698 Rugby

1699 7/6d was the cost of a marriage licence

1700 A farewell speech

1701 David Hockney

1702 *Salome*

1703 Krypton

1704 Igor Stravinsky

1705 All on a summer's day

1706 They are two sword lengths apart

1707 Banknotes and cheques

1708 Wiltshire

1709 Willy-nilly

1710 Sam Spade

1711 Vitamin C

1712 Antipodes

1713 San Marino

1714 Norwich

1715 The Queen Mother

1716 Rod Laver

1717 Access

1718 5 millilitres

1719 Prawn

1720 Raymond Chandler

1721 The end justifies the means

1722 Pommel

1723 Marlborough

1724 Bloomsbury

1725 World Professional Snooker Championship

1726 Eric Coates

1727 Caesar's

1728 A strait or channel

1729 Barbara Cartland

1730 Lear

1731 *Charlie and the Chocolate Factory*

1732 Bread and circuses

1733 Charles I

1734 Home Secretary

1735 Perspex

1736 Billiards; snooker

1737 *The Burghers of Calais*

1738 It was founded by an Englishman

1739 A dead parrot

1740 Joanna Lumley

1741 Greg Norman

1742 Skye

1743 Bristol

1744 Richard Wagner

1745 Avon lady

1746 1920s

1747 The Rubik's Cube

1748 Cloud Cuckoo Land

1749 24

1750 Monty Python's Flying Circus

1751 Thirty pieces of silver

1752 *Sleepless in Seattle*

1753 His ear

1754 Kent

1755 British Temperance Society

1756 The Atlantic Ocean

1757 The Romans

1758 Fagin

1759 The Theory of Evolution

1760 An Act of God

1761 Lambeth

1762 Mufti

1763 It is the day of the Inauguration of the President of the United States

1764 The Indian Ocean

1765 Pontius Pilate

1766 She was turned into a pillar of salt

1767 Beneath one's dignity

1768 Alexandra Palace

1769 The Dogger Bank

1770 Desert Orchid

1771 Battersea Dogs' Home

1772 'Cav and Peg'

1773 Shergar

1774 Speaker of the House of Commons

1775 Miss Marple

1776 Extra-Sensory Perception

1777 Manse

1778 They are named after saints

1779 G-string

1780 Schadenfreude

1781 *Gone With the Wind*

1782 Teachers

1783 Yeti

1784 *The Thieving Magpie*

1785 Watergate

1786 Liza Minnelli

1787 Cardiff

1788 Clio

1789 Save our Shires

1790 1970s

1791 Hovis

1792 Ungulate

1793 *Starlight Express*

1794 The Nobel Prize for Literature

1795 The brain

1796 Horse racing

1797 Tom Hanks

1798 River Rhine

1799 Darby and Joan Club

1800 Clifton Suspension Bridge

1801 National Sports Centres

1802 A rainbow

1803 *The Beano*

1804 Public Sector Borrowing Requirement

1805 Wessex

1806 *Romeo and Juliet*

1807 Loincloth

1808 Wiener schnitzel

1809 Because he wouldn't say his prayers

1810 Al Capone

1811 HMS *Beagle*

1812 Three

1813 Ogilvy

1814 Lockjaw

1815 Cleave

1816 Tennis

1817 The Ten Commandments

1818 Pointer

1819 Thames Flood Barrier

1820 Corsica, Sardinia

1821 *Pilgrim's Progress*

1822 Turin

1823 The San Andreas Fault

1824 Boris Becker

1825 Schooner

1826 Mary Queen of Scots

1827 A lower second is a 2:2, (Tutu, as in Desmond)

1828 Ran a mile in under four minutes

1829 Lacrimal glands

1830 Parental Guidance

1831 *West Side Story*

1832 The Sinai Peninsula

1833 1 ton

1834 Tomato

1835 *The Rocky Horror Picture Show*

1836 Highest and lowest elevations in the USA

1837 Shell

1838 Rebirth

1839 Community Service Volunteers

1840 A

1841 Water

1842 Wedge

1843 Strike the same place twice

1844 1950s

1845 Three years old

1846 A.A. Milne

1847 The *Mona Lisa*

1848 Viola, cello

1849 Lenny Henry

1850 Aperture

1851 Right-angled triangle

1852 Snooker

1853 Durham

1854 Handshaking

1855 Juliet

1856 *The Wizard of Oz*

1857 Charles de Gaulle

1858 Romulus and Remus

1859 The St Valentine's Day Massacre

1860 Winnie the Pooh

1861 Mackintosh

1862 Woodstock

1863 18

1864 Zambezi

1865 The Netherlands

1866 Protractor

1867 Madonna

1868 16

1869 Numbers one to eight

1870 Wilfred Owen

1871 Glenn Close

1872 VE Day and VJ Day

1873 Munster

1874 *Titanic*

1875 Port

1876 Ivan the Terrible

1877 Golf

1878 Hughes

1879 Nectar

1880 A billionth

1881 Arkansas

1882 China

1883 All cars must stop

1884 Seven

1885 Todd Carty

1886 Horatio Nelson

1887 Department stores

1888 Squash

1889 Leicestershire, Lancashire, Lincolnshire

1890 Bacterium

1891 Catherine of Aragon

1892 Muppets

1893 *The Importance of Being Earnest*

1894 Jaundice

1895 A fast-moving wave caused by an underwater earthquake

1896 Perambulator

1897 November

1898 A Cockney

1899 The Grand Old Duke of York

1900 The Spanish Armada

1901 Spain

1902 *The Three Musketeers*

1903 Oscar Wilde

1904 Cheltenham

1905 Walter Mitty

1906 Wenceslas

1907 Haggis

1908 Abraham Lincoln

1909 Iris

1910 York

1911 Leonardo DiCaprio

1912 Sleepwalking

1913 Parking meters

1914 King's Cross

1915 The Warsaw Pact

1916 The Delphic Oracle

1917 Northumberland

1918 A small island off the south of the Isle of Man

1919 Dummy

1920 1960s

1921 The American Declaration of Independence

1922 *The Water Babies*

1923 Princess Anne

1924 MGM

1925 Because the tribes of Israel are enumerated in it

1926 1940s

1927 Gall bladder

1928 '... hang separately'

1929 Corn Laws

1930 With its tail between its legs

1931 Tellers

1932 Peach

1933 Rhode Island

1934 Elizabeth I, James I, Charles I

1935 Barabbas

1936 Orson Welles

1937 Wyoming

1938 Canada

1939 Cana

1940 Botany Bay

1941 Increasing rainfall

1942 The Hellfire Club

1943 California

1944 From 65 to 70 years of age

1945 Cribbage

1946 Abacus

1947 The California Gold Rush

1948 St Petersburg

1949 Microlight

1950 Philately

1951 Northumberland, Cumbria

1952 Horse chestnut

1953 Bishop

1954 Asquith

1955 Brogue

1956 Harold Pinter

1957 David Mellor

1958 Three-eighths

1959 Anton Chekov

1960 Neighbourhood Watch

1961 A glove

1962 Dublin

1963 Saudi Arabia

1964 Traitors Gate

1965 13

1966 John Prescott

1967 Nile

1968 St Swithin

1969 They are political
     assassins

1970 Liverpool

1971 Publishing

1972 Blood

1973 *The Enigma Variations*

1974 Three-line whip

1975 Swiss

1976 The Bank of England

1977 Pilot

1978 Royal Greenwich
     Observatory

1979 *Lorne Doone*

1980 *Oliver Twist*

1981 Sunset Boulevard

1982 Toulouse-Lautrec

1983 '... an even break'

1984 Soliloquy

1985 Cornwall

1986 The Appian Way

1987 Stan Laurel

1988 Jane

1989 Walt Disney

1990 Gavin Maxwell's

1991 150

1992 Neil Kinnock

1993 Silo

1994 Mrs Worthington

1995 Poll

1996 Canaletto

1997 Ladies Day

1998 *Murder on the Orient
     Express*

1999 A sundial

2000 One third

15 to 1

Scoresheets

HOW TO USE THE
ROUNDS ONE & TWO
Scoresheets

The questionmaster should shade in the bars as the players lose their lives.

PLAYER 1

Name

PLAYER 2

Name

PLAYER 3

Name

PLAYER 4

Name

PLAYER 5

Name

PLAYER 6

Name

PLAYER 7

Name

PLAYER 8

Name

PLAYER 9

Name

PLAYER 10

Name

PLAYER 11

Name

PLAYER 12

Name

PLAYER 13

Name

PLAYER 14

Name

PLAYER 15

Name

PLAYER 1

Name

PLAYER 2

Name

PLAYER 3

Name

PLAYER 4

Name

PLAYER 5

Name

PLAYER 6

Name

PLAYER 7

Name

PLAYER 8

Name

PLAYER 9

Name

PLAYER 10

Name

PLAYER 11

Name

PLAYER 12

Name

PLAYER 13

Name

PLAYER 14

Name

PLAYER 15

Name

PLAYER 1
Name

PLAYER 2
Name

PLAYER 3
Name

PLAYER 4
Name

PLAYER 5
Name

PLAYER 6
Name

PLAYER 7
Name

PLAYER 8
Name

PLAYER 9
Name

PLAYER 10
Name

PLAYER 11
Name

PLAYER 12
Name

PLAYER 13
Name

PLAYER 14
Name

PLAYER 15
Name

PLAYER 1

Name

PLAYER 2

Name

PLAYER 3

Name

PLAYER 4

Name

PLAYER 5

Name

PLAYER 6

Name

PLAYER 7

Name

PLAYER 8

Name

PLAYER 9

Name

PLAYER 10

Name

PLAYER 11

Name

PLAYER 12

Name

PLAYER 13

Name

PLAYER 14

Name

PLAYER 15

Name

PLAYER 1
Name

PLAYER 2
Name

PLAYER 3
Name

PLAYER 4
Name

PLAYER 5
Name

PLAYER 6
Name

PLAYER 7
Name

PLAYER 8
Name

PLAYER 9
Name

PLAYER 10
Name

PLAYER 11
Name

PLAYER 12
Name

PLAYER 13
Name

PLAYER 14
Name

PLAYER 15
Name

PLAYER 1

Name

PLAYER 2

Name

PLAYER 3

Name

PLAYER 4

Name

PLAYER 5

Name

PLAYER 6

Name

PLAYER 7

Name

PLAYER 8

Name

PLAYER 9

Name

PLAYER 10

Name

PLAYER 11

Name

PLAYER 12

Name

PLAYER 13

Name

PLAYER 14

Name

PLAYER 15

Name

PLAYER 1
Name

PLAYER 2
Name

PLAYER 3
Name

PLAYER 4
Name

PLAYER 5
Name

PLAYER 6
Name

PLAYER 7
Name

PLAYER 8
Name

PLAYER 9
Name

PLAYER 10
Name

PLAYER 11
Name

PLAYER 12
Name

PLAYER 13
Name

PLAYER 14
Name

PLAYER 15
Name

HOW TO USE THE
ROUND THREE
Scoresheets

The questionmaster should shade in the bars as players lose their lives.

A player is awarded 10 points for every correct answer. As points are scored, the question master should strike through the relevant boxes.

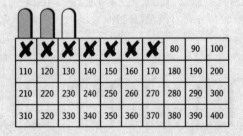

X	X	X	X	X	X	X	80	90	100
110	120	130	140	150	160	170	180	190	200
210	220	230	240	250	260	270	280	290	300
310	320	330	340	350	360	370	380	390	400

Name _____

10	20	30	40	50	60	70	80	90	100
110	120	130	140	150	160	170	180	190	200
210	220	230	240	250	260	270	280	290	300
310	320	330	340	350	360	370	380	390	400

Name _____

10	20	30	40	50	60	70	80	90	100
110	120	130	140	150	160	170	180	190	200
210	220	230	240	250	260	270	280	290	300
310	320	330	340	350	360	370	380	390	400

Name _____

10	20	30	40	50	60	70	80	90	100
110	120	130	140	150	160	170	180	190	200
210	220	230	240	250	260	270	280	290	300
310	320	330	340	350	360	370	380	390	400

Name

10	20	30	40	50	60	70	80	90	100
110	120	130	140	150	160	170	180	190	200
210	220	230	240	250	260	270	280	290	300
310	320	330	340	350	360	370	380	390	400

Name

10	20	30	40	50	60	70	80	90	100
110	120	130	140	150	160	170	180	190	200
210	220	230	240	250	260	270	280	290	300
310	320	330	340	350	360	370	380	390	400

Name

10	20	30	40	50	60	70	80	90	100
110	120	130	140	150	160	170	180	190	200
210	220	230	240	250	260	270	280	290	300
310	320	330	340	350	360	370	380	390	400

Name _____

10	20	30	40	50	60	70	80	90	100
110	120	130	140	150	160	170	180	190	200
210	220	230	240	250	260	270	280	290	300
310	320	330	340	350	360	370	380	390	400

Name _____

10	20	30	40	50	60	70	80	90	100
110	120	130	140	150	160	170	180	190	200
210	220	230	240	250	260	270	280	290	300
310	320	330	340	350	360	370	380	390	400

Name _____

10	20	30	40	50	60	70	80	90	100
110	120	130	140	150	160	170	180	190	200
210	220	230	240	250	260	270	280	290	300
310	320	330	340	350	360	370	380	390	400

Name

10	20	30	40	50	60	70	80	90	100
110	120	130	140	150	160	170	180	190	200
210	220	230	240	250	260	270	280	290	300
310	320	330	340	350	360	370	380	390	400

Name

10	20	30	40	50	60	70	80	90	100
110	120	130	140	150	160	170	180	190	200
210	220	230	240	250	260	270	280	290	300
310	320	330	340	350	360	370	380	390	400

Name

10	20	30	40	50	60	70	80	90	100
110	120	130	140	150	160	170	180	190	200
210	220	230	240	250	260	270	280	290	300
310	320	330	340	350	360	370	380	390	400

Name _____

10	20	30	40	50	60	70	80	90	100
110	120	130	140	150	160	170	180	190	200
210	220	230	240	250	260	270	280	290	300
310	320	330	340	350	360	370	380	390	400

Name _____

10	20	30	40	50	60	70	80	90	100
110	120	130	140	150	160	170	180	190	200
210	220	230	240	250	260	270	280	290	300
310	320	330	340	350	360	370	380	390	400

Name _____

10	20	30	40	50	60	70	80	90	100
110	120	130	140	150	160	170	180	190	200
210	220	230	240	250	260	270	280	290	300
310	320	330	340	350	360	370	380	390	400

Name _____

10	20	30	40	50	60	70	80	90	100
110	120	130	140	150	160	170	180	190	200
210	220	230	240	250	260	270	280	290	300
310	320	330	340	350	360	370	380	390	400

Name _____

10	20	30	40	50	60	70	80	90	100
110	120	130	140	150	160	170	180	190	200
210	220	230	240	250	260	270	280	290	300
310	320	330	340	350	360	370	380	390	400

Name _____

10	20	30	40	50	60	70	80	90	100
110	120	130	140	150	160	170	180	190	200
210	220	230	240	250	260	270	280	290	300
310	320	330	340	350	360	370	380	390	400

Name

10	20	30	40	50	60	70	80	90	100
110	120	130	140	150	160	170	180	190	200
210	220	230	240	250	260	270	280	290	300
310	320	330	340	350	360	370	380	390	400

Name

10	20	30	40	50	60	70	80	90	100
110	120	130	140	150	160	170	180	190	200
210	220	230	240	250	260	270	280	290	300
310	320	330	340	350	360	370	380	390	400

Name

10	20	30	40	50	60	70	80	90	100
110	120	130	140	150	160	170	180	190	200
210	220	230	240	250	260	270	280	290	300
310	320	330	340	350	360	370	380	390	400

Name

10	20	30	40	50	60	70	80	90	100
110	120	130	140	150	160	170	180	190	200
210	220	230	240	250	260	270	280	290	300
310	320	330	340	350	360	370	380	390	400

Name

10	20	30	40	50	60	70	80	90	100
110	120	130	140	150	160	170	180	190	200
210	220	230	240	250	260	270	280	290	300
310	320	330	340	350	360	370	380	390	400

Name

10	20	30	40	50	60	70	80	90	100
110	120	130	140	150	160	170	180	190	200
210	220	230	240	250	260	270	280	290	300
310	320	330	340	350	360	370	380	390	400

Name

10	20	30	40	50	60	70	80	90	100
110	120	130	140	150	160	170	180	190	200
210	220	230	240	250	260	270	280	290	300
310	320	330	340	350	360	370	380	390	400

Name

10	20	30	40	50	60	70	80	90	100
110	120	130	140	150	160	170	180	190	200
210	220	230	240	250	260	270	280	290	300
310	320	330	340	350	360	370	380	390	400

Name

10	20	30	40	50	60	70	80	90	100
110	120	130	140	150	160	170	180	190	200
210	220	230	240	250	260	270	280	290	300
310	320	330	340	350	360	370	380	390	400

Player	Score
Name	
Name	
Name	
Name	
Name	
Name	
Name	
Name	
Name	
Name	
Name	
Name	
Name	
Name	
Name	

Player	**Score**
Name	
Name	
Name	
Name	
Name	
Name	
Name	
Name	
Name	
Name	
Name	
Name	
Name	
Name	

Player	Score
Name	
Name	
Name	
Name	
Name	
Name	
Name	
Name	
Name	
Name	
Name	
Name	
Name	
Name	
Name	